OCEAN POLITICS AND POLICY

A Reference Handbook

Other Titles in ABC-CLIO's
CONTEMPORARY
WORLD ISSUES
Series

Books in the Contemporary World Issues series address vital issues in today's society such as genetic engineering, pollution, and biodiversity. Written by professional writers, scholars, and nonacademic experts, these books are authoritative, clearly written, up-to-date, and objective. They provide a good starting point for research by high school and college students, scholars, and general readers as well as by legislators, businesspeople, activists, and others.

Each book, carefully organized and easy to use, contains an overview of the subject, a detailed chronology, biographical sketches, facts and data and/or documents and other primary-source material, a directory of organizations and agencies, annotated lists of print and nonprint resources, and an index.

Readers of books in the Contemporary World Issues series will find the information they need in order to have a better understanding of the social, political, environmental, and economic issues facing the world today.

OCEAN POLITICS AND POLICY

A Reference Handbook

Peter Jacques and Zachary A. Smith

CONTEMPORARY WORLD ISSUES

ABC-CLIO

Santa Barbara, California
Denver, Colorado
Oxford, England

Library of Congress Cataloging-in-Publication Data

Jacques, Peter.
 Ocean politics and policy : a reference handbook / Peter Jacques and Zachary A. Smith.
    p. cm. -- (Contemporary world issues)
Includes bibliographical references and index.
 ISBN 1-57607-622-9 (acid-free paper); 1-57607-623-7 (eBook)
1. Oceanography and state. 2. Marine resources--Government policy.
I. Smith, Zachary A. (Zachary Alden), 1953- II. Title. III. Series.

GC64.J33 2003
333.91'64--dc21

                                                2002156284

06 05 04 03 02   10 9 8 7 6 5 4 3 2 1

This book is also available on the World Wide Web as an e-book. Visit abc-clio.com for details.

ABC-CLIO, Inc.
130 Cremona Drive, P.O. Box 1911
Santa Barbara, California 93116-1911

This book is printed on acid-free paper ∞.

Manufactured in the United States of America

To my parents, Earnest and Bonnie Jacques, whose confidence has been an essential and fulfilling part of my life and work—P.J.

To Leila Smith, my always supportive mother—Z.S.

Contents

Preface

J ames Rosenau has written that the world is at once fragment-
ing and integrating at the same time, and this seems to be an
appropriate observation regarding the World Ocean. Spaces
that once were distant are now connected, ecosystems that once
were seen as separate are now seen as whole, and policies of one
country are now important to many. At the same time, divisive
power politics troubles this integration.

The seemingly permanent interests of industry, governments, agencies, and councils continually and predictably push
the limits of fish stocks for yields that have proven to be anything
but sustainable. Climate change has hinted at the twilight of
hydrocarbon economies, but powerful forces deny policy change
on the matter. Biodiversity loss profoundly threatens to alter the
depth of life on Earth; in the World Ocean, loss of individual
species such as fish have made some areas a garden of sea nettles.
More important, ageless structures that harbor some of the rich-
est biodiversity in the world—coral reefs—are on the chopping
block of history as we speak. Coastal communities are quickly
growing in population density at the same time that sea-level rise
and catastrophic natural disasters make them more vulnerable. In
other words, as Zachary Smith has argued for many years now,
we are faced with an array of environmental policy paradoxes.
Answers to these environmental problems are available at this
very moment, but power, money, and other political factors consistently drive collective action away from practical and workable
solutions.

This book looks at several of the most important problems
within the World Ocean. The term *World Ocean* is used purposefully to direct attention to the holism of this ecosystem. Geography
has named several main oceanic bodies, but the tangible borders
between one and another are illusory. Organisms, currents, and

pollutants flow between these bodies with the same regard for artificial boundaries that an eagle has for national borders.

This thinking is not new or pioneering. Indeed, the main document regarding the World Ocean, the United Nations Convention on the Law of the Sea, was negotiated and drafted in exactly this spirit. The Law of the Sea provides ocean politics with another important benchmark and is discussed in the first chapter of this book. The politics of the World Ocean continues to change, for the ocean has been transformed from an open resource to more of a true common-pool resource, where access and use are increasingly subject to intervention. The community in charge of this common-pool resource is the international community, which has seen itself as anarchic since the inception of the *mare liberum* doctrine. Imposing policy within anarchy is something of a tricky matter, infused with the interests of great powers, military ambition, and unbridled greed. Again, the notions of integration and fragmentation make sense. This book attempts to fully explain these forces of world politics in regard to *mare nostrum*—our ocean.

Since the World Ocean is a stage for international relations, it is also a space where security is negotiated. The matter of "ocean security" is taken seriously in this volume; indeed, one chapter is devoted to the topic. Here, ocean security is divided into two basic areas—traditional and ecological. Traditional security is concerned with familiar security demands of deterrence, stability, and armed conflict. Ecological security, by contrast, is more elusive but increasingly in the minds of security analysts everywhere. This is the notion that taking care of the World Ocean ecologically is a matter of survival for the human race. Quite simply, human treatment of oceanic conditions reflects directly back to our own condition of well-being in a way that relates to the nature of humankind's very existence. Placing ocean politics into this frame of reference means that solving the environmental policy paradoxes mentioned earlier is a serious project of the utmost urgency.

That being said, this book is a primer. It is designed to be a foundational starting point for students, bureaucrats, policymakers, and others who need to acquire basic information and have terms explained. Many readers will come to this book with no prior knowledge of ocean politics. However, some new topics are provided in this volume that even those who are well versed in ocean politics will find interesting and important. The first is the treatment of ocean security, described earlier. The second is the matter of migratory and transboundary fisheries. The fishery problem itself is not new, but this is the first primer that we are aware of that deals with and describes the effects of the Fishery Stock Agreement (FSA), which went into force at the end of 2001. The FSA provides the newest grounds for sustainable management of the world's transboundary and migratory fish stocks, and it addresses key problems that have previously derailed attempts at sound fishery management, such as the "flags of convenience" problem. All of these issues are described in the following chapters.

This book also provides directions for more in-depth research. Within these pages, the reader will find descriptions and histories of key figures and events, data on some important oceanographic conditions, full-text sections of key treaties and agreements, descriptions and contacts for prominent ocean groups and agencies, and many references for both print and nonprint resources.

1

Currents in Ocean Politics: Oceans in Context

For about four hundred years, "the freedom of the seas" doctrine prevailed in matters related to the world's oceans. Now, however, at the start of the twenty-first century, that doctrine has been eclipsed by "the law of the seas." This chapter will show how and why this evolution occurred. In addition, common-pool resource management and international regimes will be discussed in order to introduce the dominant principles of international ocean governance. At the end of the chapter, the structure and reasoning for the rest of the book will be presented. But the first task at hand is to define and explore the concepts of ocean politics and policy.

Ocean Politics and Policy

Politics involves the dynamic phenomena of influence in social life. It includes the ways in which people organize themselves and make decisions. Fundamentally, politics pertains to power in society, encompassing the questions of how power is used and arranged, who has and does not have significant power, and the effects of power arrangements in society.

Ocean politics is as complex and deep as the ocean itself, but that does not mean the topic is difficult to comprehend. On the contrary, even though some of the issues in this book will be new to readers, many of the influences that pertain to the ocean also surround our daily lives and are quite familiar. This book attempts to systematically describe and analyze the important parts of ocean politics and place them in an easily understood context.

Ocean *politics* deals with the struggle for values, resources, and power in relation to the ocean. Ocean *policies* are the decisions that are made regarding what to do (or not do) about any set of ocean-related issues. In general, ocean policy is driven by ocean politics. However, there is no neat separation between politics and policy. Ocean politics and ocean policy often entail the same struggles.

To understand a complex subject, it is sometimes wise to break that subject into parts. For this reason, the broader subject of ocean politics will be divided into two foundations here: environmental politics and security politics. This division is arbitrary and artificial, but, in fact, most if not all matters of ocean politics relate to one of these two major categories.

Both environmental politics and security politics involve human relationships. Traditional environmental policy has typically focused on human relationships to nature, whereas traditional security policy has tended to center on human survival and violence (for example, interstate wars). One of the main points of this book is that it is now understood that human relationships to nature are inextricably intertwined with human survival and can be related to human violence as well. The two foundations are coming together such that environmental politics is now a permanent part of security politics. This relatively new advance in social science is discussed thoroughly in the third chapter of this text. The environmental and security foundations of ocean politics will now be discussed in more detail, followed by a note on the role science plays in the making of marine policy.

Ocean Politics as Environmental Politics

Environmental politics involves the struggles between people about how they relate to nature. The scope of environmental politics encompasses history, economics, psychology, ecology, and international affairs, to name but a few dimensions. Consequently, environmental politics is a universal area of study that has to do with everything involving people and nature.

Although ocean politics is only one part of environmental politics, the World Ocean is perhaps the planet's most important environmental asset. The ocean makes up the largest portion (about 71 percent) of the earth's surface, and it holds about 97 percent of the world's water supply. The ocean also provides about 99 percent of the world's habitat, given that most land species only live on the surface whereas ocean species exist throughout the entire depth and expanse of the ocean. Simply put, the ocean is an environmental resource and habitat of huge magnitude.

In determining how the ocean should be governed and treated, a host of questions must be addressed. How many sharks, if any, should people be allowed to kill each year and why? What limits should be set in developing a coastline? How much human-caused ocean pollution is acceptable? What should be done about rising sea levels? How much energy should be devoted to preserving coral reefs? Are whales highly evolved, sentient beings that should never be hunted with exploding harpoons? Who does the wealth of the World Ocean belong to? The list of questions, many of them seemingly unrelated, is long. These are the topics of environmental politics and the ocean, and this book provides some background to a few of the most pressing of these questions in chapter 2.

Ocean Politics as Security Politics

Security politics is the politics of physical survival. Whether the context involves naval forces that promote military security or the ecological goods and services that come from the ocean and promote life, a continuous foundation for ocean politics has been the politics of survival. Deciding what to do about problems of survival, such as war and violence, is a matter of security policy; so, too, are judgments made about what ocean resources must be preserved for human survival.

Security policy has traditionally entailed strategic military planning. These and related questions still pervade security politics. In developing a military strategy and building forces to counter perceived threats, a wide array of questions must be posed. Who is a threat? What nations or groups have hostile intent? What are the military abilities of a given nation or group? What are the results of arms races? What is the balance of conventional and nuclear weapons in the world? Who controls sea-lanes in vital areas?" The ocean is incredibly important in formulating hypotheses and answers to such questions because so many interstate military disputes occur through marine avenues. For example, half of the nuclear warheads maintained by the United States are on naval ships (including submarines) and can be launched at any coast those ships can access. Also, there is a solid correlation between nations that are strong at sea and those that are strong economically.

Although such straightforward military concerns persist, security politics has changed since the early 1970s and now includes environmental security, or the environmental features that affect human survival and cooperation. Because the ocean is a foundation for life itself on the planet, the possibility of disrupting this foundation is a serious security concern and an important focus of this book.

The Role of Science in Ocean Politics

As noted earlier in this chapter, ocean policy is driven by ocean politics. But contrary to what one might intuitively assume, oceanography, marine biology, and other ecological sciences by themselves do not determine ocean policy. This observation requires an explanation about the role of science in the policy-making process. First, however, consider the following example of the part science has played in global-warming policy.

In June 2002, the *New York Times* reported that President George Bush's administration had changed its policy regarding global warming. Previous policy statements made by the president indicated that he would not abide by the Kyoto Protocol to limit greenhouse gases. He said that the science regarding the real causes of global warming was uncertain and that the actual fact of global warming had not been fully examined; consequently, President Bush said it was not in the country's interest to reduce the greenhouse gases being emitted by the oil-dependent U.S. economy. However, in a report filed quietly with the United Nations (and unearthed by the *New York Times*), the Bush administration admitted that global warming would actually cause substantial ecological and social changes to the United States. Contrary to what some climate scientists might have expected, the administration's report did not say that it would change direction on emissions but that people should prepare for and adapt to these coming climate and ecological changes. Consequently, the political interests of the administration determined climate and energy policy more than the scientific work that challenged this controversial stand. This story is not an unusual one.

Science provides knowledge about the natural world, and ocean science in particular provides good information about the ocean world. But as in the global-warming example, policymakers do not always pursue policies that seem obvious. Zachary Smith (2001) has called this an environmental policy paradox.

Typically, scientists can identify several appropriate solutions that could be applied to an environmental problem, but often, those solutions are not used, for various reasons. The reasons include dominant cultural attitudes and values when they conflict with what good science tells us to do and incentives (such as money or political gain) that promote inappropriate alternatives. At other times, people in opposition to a particular remedy simply out-muscle those on the other side of the struggle.

Because policy is about making decisions regarding human actions, human desires inevitably come into play. Consequently, it may actually be preferable if science alone does *not* dictate ocean policy; with its empirical conclusions, physical science cannot, for instance, comment on democratic decisionmaking or the distribution of wealth. The desirable effects of making political decisions may be lost if policy is driven by science.

But if politics determines policy, how does science operate in the policymaking process? Fundamentally, science produces knowledge. However, knowledge is used in politics to promote specific agendas, meaning that some science is highlighted and other science is purposefully neglected, depending on the ability of the scientific conclusions to serve a given agenda. It is also true that policy prescriptions do not always flow clearly from scientific research, since policymakers can usually proceed in several different and contradictory directions on the basis of the same scientific information. Beyond that, science itself is uncertain and not immune to politics.

The global-warming story illustrates these points. First, political influence determined what to do with the scientific information that showed the world was warmer than before, and there was evidence of gases in the atmosphere that offered a plausible hypothesis—humans were cooking the planet. The information in this case was not ignored, but the policy initiatives offered (adapting to climate change) probably would have confounded climatologists. Second, the policymaking community as represented in President Bush's statements implied that it would wait for certainty to act on global-warming problems, if it acted at all. However, scientists know that absolute certainty is rare in science and is reserved for special cases—gravity, for example. Issues such as exactly how human emissions affect climate change will not approach certainty for a very, very long time, if ever.

In fact, good science acknowledges where the most uncertainty resides in scientific findings. And waiting for certainty in policy is a good way to endorse the status quo and do nothing.

Even if doing nothing sounds like a rational decision, it also means putting off any change to an existing policy, which more than likely is also not based on any scientific certainty.

Studies on marine ecosystems are especially burdened with uncertainty. Human knowledge about the ocean is trivial compared to what is left to be understood. We have only explored about 5 percent of the ocean, and in that small area, our understanding of how ecosystems interrelate is fragile at best. Another complicating factor is the increasing frequency of serious changes imposed by human activity, such as the clearing of mangrove forests, the destruction of coral reefs, and the loss of biodiversity.

Since the repercussions of these impacts are unclear, proceeding on a course that entails any degree of environmental impact is a grand experiment. Moreover, profound effects of our grand experiments may go unnoticed until it is too late, for we do not have the ability to easily observe most of the ocean. For instance, deep thermohaline currents (currents that operate by means of their saline content and temperature) run at the bottom of the ocean at about 2°C and at 1 millimeter a second (35.6°F and .039 inches a second)—thus taking about a thousand years to circle the globe. These currents keep the earth's temperature stable, but there is evidence that they will change along with global warming. Ocean research into phenomena of this type can be difficult, however, and its results very unsure (Wood et al. 1999). How many samples from how many sites do we need for the research to be compelling? How long do we wait to do something about such a revelation, if we do anything at all? How do we know changes in these currents do not naturally occur every three hundred years? Marine science is better and more sophisticated than it has ever been, but it is also fraught with uncertainty, perhaps more so than other scientific endeavors because the deep blue hides a lot of evidence. This problem is a part of ocean politics.

In the end, scientists themselves have to make political choices about what questions are the important ones to study. As Sheila Jasonoff (1998, 155) wrote, "When it comes to studying the causes of complex environmental problems, there is almost always more than one way to skin the scientific cat. And these choices are not themselves scientific. They're deeply social, cultural, and ethical." (One could add "economic" as well.) In conclusion, for better or worse, the role of science in policymaking is necessary but not in itself sufficient to guide that endeavor.

Mare Liberum: The Open Oceans

Now that the scope of ocean politics has been defined, the history of international ocean law will be addressed, starting with the doctrine of the freedom of the seas. In 1609, Hugo Grotius wrote one of the most important international legal doctrines regarding the oceans—*Mare Liberum*, a Latin title that translates to "the freedom of the seas." The main point of *Mare Liberum* was that the oceans, specifically the high seas (those areas of the ocean beyond the control of any country), could not be owned by any person or nation. Consequently, the oceans were free for anyone to use and exploit without limits. Grotius was primarily concerned with the navigation of the oceans and keeping shipping lanes open, but the effect of his doctrine expanded to all uses, such as fishing and other industry. Grotius's notion of the freedom of the seas would persist until the mid-twentieth century, and it continues to be applied even to this day for much of the high seas, though the application of the concept and the scope of its reach is surely changing, as this chapter will document.

The territorial seas were the only exception to the mare liberum doctrine. Territorial seas were defined as the waters that extended from the low tide of a coastal nation outward for a distance of 3 nautical miles (a nautical mile is 6,076 feet, which is slightly longer than the 5,280-foot terrestrial mile). The 3-mile limit was not an arbitrary designation. It was the distance a cannonball could be fired; thus, a nation could own that area. Such was the beginning of international ocean law.

The primary assumption inherent in the notion of the freedom of the seas was that the ocean's resources were inexhaustible. Nations saw the World Ocean as unlimited in its vast stretches of space, unlimited in its marine life, and unlimited in its ability to take on new users and waste. Fisheries (areas that are fished) were seen to be so plentiful, for example, that human endeavor could not conceivably affect the numbers of fish available. Therefore, setting limits on fishing seemed a ludicrous idea at best and an economically damaging one at worst. As this assumption came to be challenged by reports of low fish catches by fishers and some preliminary scientific studies in the 1800s, members of the international community began to move toward protecting resources that they considered commercially important to their own interests.

By that time, the oceans of the world were primarily under-stood in international terms. It was beginning to become obvious that what one country did on or to the ocean fundamentally affected what other countries could do with it. Nonetheless, it was not until the late nineteenth century that the doctrine of the free seas was seriously questioned internationally, and only in 1958 was the doctrine limited in any way by multilateral international laws.

Historically, the prevailing international view of the oceans has been tied to concepts of relatively unrestricted, open use. Thus, most international ocean laws exist as exceptions to that freedom. In the second half of the twentieth century, limiting or putting boundaries on this freedom was the primary task of the United Nations Convention on the Law of the Sea (UNCLOS). There were actually three such conventions, starting in 1958 with UNCLOS-I and ending in 1982 with UNCLOS-III. The premier concern for each of these conventions was how to manage the well-established freedom of the seas in light of new knowledge that proved the oceans were more fragile than previously thought.

Ocean management, which usually means either limiting or encouraging various human practices that affect the oceans, is fundamentally in conflict with the notion of the freedom of the seas. Other tensions exist as well, for certain goals of ocean management compete with each other. For instance, the goals of achieving national security, commercially harvesting marine resources, and preserving ecological integrity can all be pursued simultaneously in ocean management, but they may compete against each other in both national and international policies. To cite one example, it was argued during and after World War II that U.S. national security was dependent on drilling for oil on the continental shelf. Since oil spills are an unfortunate part of drilling and transporting oil, the health of those same coastal ecosystems was obviously considered secondary. Therefore, ocean management really refers to creating sustainable concepts of nature while balancing and managing human behavior vis-à-vis the oceans according to the political influences of the time. Internationally, this has been accomplished through multilateral regimes, which are discussed later in this chapter.

Common-Pool Resources

The freedom of the seas makes the ownership of the international oceans global. Resources that are used and held jointly, such as the international oceans, are called "common-pool resources." Garrett Hardin (1968), who shaped the way common-pool resources are understood, used the example of a field shared by herders to explain why managing common-pool resources is a challenge.

The health of the field in Hardin's example depends largely on the agreements and behaviors of the herders. If the use of the field is free or without some limits, he argued, there is no incentive for any one herder to limit his or her own grazing. But since the field can only handle a certain amount of use, which is true of most ecosystems, unlimited grazing by all herders will collapse the field ecosystem. Hardin called this outcome "the tragedy of the commons."

Under this scenario, there are no costs to using the resource, and a rational individual has an incentive to use as much of that resource as possible before his or her fellow herders do the same. In this context, the term *rational* suggests that the herder considers him- or herself to be alone and separate from the other herders. Therefore, any benefits to this person are not shared with the other herders. This scenario also assumes that the benefits to each individual are viewed only in the short term. Otherwise, if each herder realized that the field would be overgrazed by other individuals who were also following their short-term interests, the truly rational thing to do would be to limit individual use. Only then would the field continue to function and support everyone. Although Hardin's article has since met with fierce and compelling criticism, the warning he offered can be applied to ocean management to some extent because nations, especially marine powers, have generally tried to get as much as they can from the ocean.

If each country uses the ocean to get as much as possible of a given commodity such as fish before any other country gets that same commodity, then the tragedy of the commons will occur. This attitude and use can risk the collapse of fisheries and the ecosystems to which those fisheries are connected, thereby endangering a vast network of dependents, including people. If, however, limits are in place to stop this from happening, then the tragedy may well be averted.

Notice that a fundamental assumption about the ocean has changed over time: we now realize that its resources, once thought infinite, are in fact finite. And ocean policy made under the assumption of limited resources is very different from that made under the assumption of infinite resources. This shift in orientation is, as noted earlier, relatively recent in human history.

Unlike the field in Hardin's example, the World Ocean has vast global importance. It provides almost three-quarters of the world's oxygen through its phytoplankton. The ocean also moderates the global temperature, keeping the earth from becoming either a ball of ice or an uninhabitable desert. Thus, the services that the World Ocean provides are essential to every living creature on the planet. If the ocean's ability to do even just these two things is disturbed, the human species and perhaps almost all others will be in jeopardy. This reality is part of what is at stake when nations are asked to limit themselves. Yet as of this writing, the United States still has not ratified the Law of the Sea and has rejected limits on its own behavior in the ocean, most notably in terms of mining in the deep seabed.

Hardin has been criticized for treating all resources as either privately held and well managed or commonly held and ill managed. Also, other scholars have noted distinctions between open-pool and common-pool resources. A common-pool resource is controlled by a community that imposes limits on the use of the resource. Benefit-sharing components as well as rules guiding resource use are often established in the common-pool situation, whereas no limits are placed on the use of an open-pool resource.

Understanding this difference, it can be said that the World Ocean went from an open resource to a combination of common-pool and open resources with the advent of the Law of the Sea. The jurisdictions set up by this law essentially divide the ocean into private, common-pool, and open areas. For example, an exclusive economic zone (EEZ), an area that extends 200 miles from a coast, can be shared but is also affected by a set of established rules that limit users and uses. Beyond that 200-mile mark, the ocean is still remarkably open, with the exception of new governance for fishing (see chapter 3). Nevertheless, the ocean is generally referred to as a common-pool resource.

The allocation of common-pool resources is guided by the principles of rival and nonrival characteristics. Resources that are not renewable are called "rival" or "exhaustible" resources, and the equitable allocation of these scarce resources requires active management. Rival resources can only be used once. Oil drilled from the continental shelf is one example of an exhaustible, rival resource because once someone drills a barrel of oil out of the Gulf of Mexico, for instance, no one else may drill that same barrel of oil, nor will that oil be replenished in the shelf. By contrast, the water through which ships navigate is deemed nonrival because it does not become depleted due to the passage of any number of vessels.

Excludable resources are those resources that allow the exclusion or separation of users. Excludable resources, then, are more easily made into private holdings. A nonexcludable resource is one that does not allow such separation and therefore also does not allow for the separation of those who pay for the resource (with money or consequences) and those who do not. In other words, free riders are considered to be a problem at times for nonexcludable resources. This is why, typically, nonexhaustibility and nonexcludability can also be used to determine that which is a public good versus that which is a private good.

The ocean waters lying beyond the limits of the territorial seas are held in public, international commons. Although some portions of the ocean may be enclosed (bays, inlets, and other land-related areas), most of the ocean (and therefore most of the surface of the earth) is considered to be a communally held resource.

Some resources in the ocean are rival, and some are not. Those that are rival engender competition among nations that are powerful enough and that have the ability to make rival resources their own (that is, to exclude them from others). In this way, mare liberum allows free access to the oceans but encourages nations to make the parts they capture private, thereby depleting the rival resources for the rest of the commons.

Though all of the nations of the world have an equally legitimate claim to the resources of the middle of the Pacific, for instance, all nations do not use it equally. Thus, part of the work of ocean management is to make both the equitable distribution of resources and the sustainable development of resources as real as possible. Equitable management is behind the idea of the "common heritage of mankind." Arvid Pardoe, a Maltese delegate to the United Nations Convention on the Law of the Sea, argued passionately that the riches of the ocean floor should belong to all nations of the world equally and even contribute to the uplift of poor nations (see chapter 2).

If management of the World Ocean is to be effective, limits must apply to the users, and these users must consider each other and the well-being of the ocean together. However, users in this context are nations as well as groups and individuals within nations. This is where regimes come into play.

International Regimes

"A regime exists when widely accepted principles and norms govern behavior. International regimes almost always have at their core an accord (also known as an agreement) that establishes specific rules, commitments, and decision making procedures to aid in the process of governance. Such accords form the core of international law" (Victor, Raustiala, and Skolnikoff 1998, 8). These agreements produce and are created by norms and principals, which in turn create decisionmaking mechanisms and frequently bureaucratic institutions. Regimes are often said to provide the basis for international ocean management, but regimes are controversial. How regimes form and continue to work (or not work) is up for debate. Some experts argue that regimes form because the presence and demands of a powerful nation force issues on weaker states or that knowledge about a topic changes and converges on obvious answers to promote international cooperation.

Regimes are complex. They may come about because one powerful and dominant nation (a hegemonic nation) provides the stability needed for agreement. Or they may be the product of a multitude of interest groups such as nongovernmental organizations (NGOs), industry, and nations coming together nonhierarchically. In either case, agreement eventually occurs because of a need that cannot be satisfied by an individual state. Even if a state is looking for short-term gains in a treaty, it is not likely to agree to something it has no need for or that it can accomplish on its own. Usually, environmental regimes emerge as a result of a conflict over a resource, creating a need to resolve the conflict peacefully in order to establish allocative rules. The Grotian treatise on the freedom of the seas was the result of a conflict over navigation rights between the British and the Dutch. Though the treatise itself was criticized by some, it was largely accepted and became an expectation internationally—a regime. Sometimes, regimes may result from the "claim/counterclaim" process of international law. This process begins when a nation makes a claim, and whether that claim is accepted or rigorously rejected by other nations can determine if it becomes international law (Juda 1996).

However, most of the time, regimes stem from international deliberations that result in treaties. Since treaties are negotiated by nation-states, this is another area of controversy for international relations theorists. Some theorists argue that discrimination or injustice that is hidden by the nation-state is not going to be resolved by nation-states cooperating. In other words, any problems caused by a system of nation-states are themselves not going to be addressed by regimes because nation-states constitute the regimes. This means, for example, if the *system* of nation-states is responsible for marine degradation, no amount of cooperation will adequately address the root problems in the system itself.

That being said, understanding regimes begins by understanding sovereignty. In its ideal and pure sense, sovereignty is the autonomy of a nation-state, and it has both external and internal facets. External sovereignty is the ability to keep other nations out of the home country and to control borders while maintaining the ability to negotiate with outside forces, such as other nation-states. Thus, external sovereignty means controlling foreign policy and borders, including coastal borders. Internal sovereignty, by contrast, means controlling the population and being able to develop laws, policies, and resources without outside influences and is called the doctrine of noninterference. Because noninterference allows countries to do almost whatever they like, regimes are sometimes weak, since external coercion, outside of war or similar sanctions, is not a typical option. Sovereignty is said to exist for nation-states because no external government has ultimate legal rule over a nation-state. If this is true, then the international world is anarchic from the state's point of view. Regimes and regime theories that emphasize the interdependence of all nations challenge this notion of anarchy because the regimes themselves provide some form of governance. Thus, each agreement a state enters into and honors confines the autonomy and sovereignty of that state. States may be willing to limit their sovereignty to stave off physical violence and attack, to safeguard a commercial activity, to protect environmental resources, and perhaps even in the name of an international common will (Reuter 1989). The latter is a central element in the Law of Treaties, which set the regime for treaties themselves and coincidentally also had its conceptual origin with Grotius. According to that law, treaties and international laws must all be ratified in each signing nation to be legally binding on a given nation, in order to confirm that the particular nations are acknowledging limits to their sovereignty.

Also, though sovereignty is usually discussed in terms of pure autonomy, the sovereignty of one state is not, in a practical sense, necessarily the same as the sovereignty (or autonomy) of another. During the Law of the Sea conventions, this point was made by nonmarine powers. Their argument ran something like the following. The freedom of the seas doctrine held that anyone who could use the sea had the right to do so. But some nations did not have the same ability to use the oceans as others, and thus, they actually could not use the sea in equal fashion. For example, nations that had steam-engine boats and ice-making capabilities could send their ships farther out than those that did not (as will be discussed in more detail). Consequently, the marine powers were exploiting the oceans for whatever purposes they could, as was their legal right. From the coastal nations' perspective, however, foreign countries were raiding their areas and resources, probably because they had used up their own. Because of situations like this, the construction of marine rights, policies, laws, and management all have allocative consequences, or consequences that distribute costs, benefits, and opportunities (Juda 1996).

Such is the volatile environment of international affairs. International law and domestic law are distinctly different in significant ways. In the United States, if someone breaks the law, the government presumably insists on corrective behavior, with the threat of coercion backing up all its demands. However, short of threatening war, states have a limited ability to enforce coercive regulations on other countries. Economic sanctions are often employed to punish offending states, but most management is done by agreement because states must, to some degree, voluntarily submit to limits on their own behaviors. A state enters an agreement and abides by its limits because it sees some advantage for itself in doing so. States are often seen as the primary actors in the world with revolving interests, but if common-pool resources such as the ocean are to be managed with real limits on real people, then nations must, at the very least, see conservation as both a short-term and long-term common goal. Of course, regimes themselves change over time, as do the conditions for the regimes. Furthermore, state interests have been shown to be more flexible than previously thought, which gives some groups a strong hand in developing values and expectations domestically (Wapner 1996). States can be swayed by environmental movements and demands. And heads of states may make concessions they would never agree to without the pressure of groups such as nongovernmental organizations, which are becoming increasingly important in international politics.

Regime Concepts for the Ocean

Ernst Haas (1983, 24) has written that the Law of the Sea regime is an artifact of changing knowledge:

The ocean regime for centuries was based on the norm of maximum open access: outside the territorial sea— whose boundary floated inexorably outward after 1945—any state could do anything. What caused the change toward fisheries conservation zones, pollution-free zones, restrictions on transit, and international controls on the mining of the deep sea? What is responsible for the norm that the oceans are "the heritage of mankind," a public good par excellence?

Haas believes that the connecting link between the drastic changes in ocean regimes reflects the way the world thinks about nature. The way a nation thinks about nature changes and is assumed to affect the way the national interests are formed. Therefore, regime norms are dependent on and evolve with the knowledge that justifies the norms and principles of the regime. The fact that the human perception of the ocean changed from one of absolute boundlessness to one of limit explains, at least in part, the change from a freedom of the seas doctrine to a law of the seas.

In the early years of marine management, as mentioned earlier, the ocean was thought to have inexhaustible resources. There seemed to be no need for limiting fish catch, ship pollution, coastal mining, and so forth; the resource in question either was technically out of reach, as in continental shelf drilling, or showed no sign of depletion. However, over time, the ability to catch fish expanded greatly, particularly with the introduction of cotton trawl nets, steam- and gasoline-powered vessels, ice to preserve the catch, and other technological advances. As a result, the scale of the world fish catch and other ocean harvests increased greatly for a short time. However, it was not until fish catches started decreasing relative to the effort put forth that some began to question the idea that the World Ocean was nonexhaustible. In the mid-1800s, scientific studies of fisheries became important, and the research showed that the ocean's resources were finite and that human endeavor had a profound effect on the ocean (for instance, on fish stocks). And once the ocean's fish became harder to catch, nations began trying to protect their share of that resource.

The first of the ocean regimes emerged between Great Britain and the United States (Juda 1996). The Treaty of Washington in 1892 established limits on seal hunting in the waters off the Pribiloff Islands, which were part of the U.S. purchase of Alaska from Russia. Great Britain had been hunting the seals in the area, and the United States seized the British ships for doing so because U.S. commercial activity was at stake. Great Britain protested the act. Eventually, the treaty established a binding arbitration mechanism between the two naval powers.

The arbitration ruled that the United States had no right to seize vessels outside its 3-mile limit; it also ruled that conservation of the seals was necessary. This was one of the first times that the 3-mile limit was shown to be insufficient for ocean management purposes. Ultimately, it was agreed that Great Britain's vessels would be banned by *British* law from pelagic, or open-sea, seal hunting within 60 miles off the Pribiloff Islands, and the same rule was applied to U.S. vessels. However, to get the British leaders to agree to this limit, in opposition to their right to a free ocean, the United States had to agree to give Britain a share of the seals hunted on land.

The treaty fell apart when Japanese and Russian vessels began hunting seals in the areas that the U.S. and British governments had restricted in terms of their own use. The seal population suffered as a result, falling from 4.7 million in 1874 to just 130,000 in 1907. Consequently, in 1911, a four-power treaty—the 1911 North Pacific Sealing Convention—was signed to limit the seal hunting of all four countries.

This agreement would set the protocol for managing ocean problems until the first United Nations Convention on the Law of the Sea in 1958. By working within its bilateral and multilateral treaty formats, conflicts over ocean use could be resolved without affecting the freedom of the seas for other nations. But nations not involved in the agreement would prove to be problematic. For instance, although a coastal nation could limit its own use of a nearby area to maintain that area's ecological integrity, other nations that were not a party to the limit could enter the area without competition. Meanwhile, nationals of the coastal country had cut themselves off from the resource in question. In the end, agreements that did not include *all* of the states using an area would become meaningless in terms of protecting the ocean. These unsuccessful treaties also became sources of tension for users whose access had been cut off.

As with the seal-hunting example, the need for more limits became apparent for resources such as fish, and nations moved to protect what they saw as their own share. Specifically, coastal states were continually at odds with "distant-water" maritime powers—the United States, Japan, Russia, Great Britain, and other countries that had the ability to send fishing fleets to far-off coasts. These fleets would sit outside the 3-mile limit and take all they could from the distant seas to carry back to home markets. Countries that did not have traditionally strong maritime fleets saw this practice as an intrusion on their sovereignty. Historically, battle lines over ocean governance and management have consistently been drawn between maritime powers and coastal states that are not maritime powers.

As international law was negotiated, maritime powers typically fought to maintain the status quo of the freedom of the seas, which would allow them to continue to take marine resources and marine life from distant areas. Coastal nations would then counter this pressure by fighting to expand the territorial seas and commercial zones so they could better control the harvesting and conservation of nearby waters.

Interestingly enough, the United States found itself in a particular bind in these negotiations. It usually fought bitterly for a continuance of the freedom of the seas doctrine. However, it also had to find ways to protect fisheries on its own coasts. In fact, two proclamations by Harry Truman's administration are credited for initiating the law of the sea.

The Truman Proclamation on the Continental Shelf and the Truman Proclamation on Fisheries were both issued in 1945. The former declared "jurisdiction and control" of the seabed and subsea soil for oil exploration and extraction, but it did not use the word sovereignty so as to not endanger U.S. foreign exploits. Similarly, it moved to protect salmon fisheries in Alaska from Japanese floating canneries by establishing the concept of "prior interest." This idea protected the U.S. fishing fleets working in foreign waters because they also had a prior interest through their historical presence there.

However, the irony of the proclamations did not escape the international community, which responded with its own demands. The predicament the United States found itself in mirrored concerns in other states, and there was a growing consensus that the 3-mile territorial sea was inadequate for conservation purposes. This scenario created a window of opportunity for coastal states to break the naval monopolies' grip on the free seas and increase their own control over local waters through enlarged territorial seas and commercial zones.

The long-standing regime of the freedom of the seas did not correspond with any ecosystem management borders, the needs of marine life, or obvious geographic zones. Rather, it was derived from the political power of a few nations. Most of the states that accepted Grotius's dictum and adopted it as international law were European nations (Portugal, Spain, Great Britain, the Netherlands, and so on). Consequently, later delegates from Asia and Africa would strongly protest the 3-mile limit by saying no one had consulted them about it. This growing dissent and shifting power arrangements would ultimately change the way the ocean was to be managed. Thus, for three hundred years, a European idea guided the norms of the ocean while much of the rest of the world was under European colonization. As the grip of colonizing nations loosened, so, too, did the grip of the freedom of the seas doctrine. But this kind of power is not the only cause for a change in a regime, for the power of participants in an agreement is an important issue and may determine a good deal about the regime itself.

In summary, control over ocean resources along the coasts was continually at issue for at least a hundred years before the international community came to an agreement on how to reform the freedom of the seas doctrine. Yet even after the third and final United Nations Convention on the Law of the Sea (1982), the high seas were still considered to be *res nullius,* or property belonging to no one, as established by Grotius.

However, the Law of the Sea has set in place the transformation of ocean politics, which continues to erode the mare liberum regime. The regime based on the freedom of the seas and open-pool resources is now changing into a common-pool resource regime managed by active regional communities. With the advent of the Fishery Stock Agreement (FSA) (see chapters 2 and 3), the freedom of the seas doctrine with regard to fishing is no longer applicable. This is a startling revision. Even as this book was being written, the freedom to fish anywhere outside national jurisdictions was revoked under certain conditions. Whether the FSA is effective is a topic left for another book, but the act of legislating a new concept for the oceans has taken place.

Ocean managers, diplomats, and scholars should all note, however, that as limits are placed on these open areas in the future, such policies will have allocative effects. Some nations will benefit more than others, and some will be entirely left out of the equation. Consequently, domestic and international policies about the ocean will always be characterized by the passionate interaction of political issues, groups, and norms as well as by the cumbersome interests of nation-states.

Organization of the Book

As a reference book, this text is divided into sections that explain ocean politics and governance from several different policy perspectives. Chapter 2 covers several ecological concerns and controversies, such as fishing, whaling, and jurisdictional problems, and it deals directly with the environmental policy aspects of ocean politics. Treating ecological problems is the goal of ocean management, though many experts in this field reasonably consider the word *management* inappropriate, since it implies that people can control the ocean. Clearly, controlling the ocean is not a plausible or desirable goal, but controlling human impacts on the ocean generally is quite desirable, and chapter 2 describes the politics behind limiting human impacts on the fragile marine environment. Chapter 2 also explains what integrated coastal management is and why it is important, how and why fishing populations are in trouble worldwide, and how commercial whaling has become banned and why it is likely to be reinstated in the near future. In addition, the problem of ocean pollution is explored with a case study of the *Exxon Valdez* spill, and a description of high-seas mining and the politics that have affected this important aspect of ocean governance is provided.

Chapter 3 examines the topic of ocean security. There, the different and important goals of ocean security are outlined. The traditional goal of ocean security is military stability. The rationale and politics of using naval power to stem the occurrence of war between nations is explained, including the aspects of conventional and nuclear deterrence. Then, the issue of piracy is explored as a nonmilitary threat to ocean security. Finally, the emerging goal of protecting ecological values as an ocean security issue is addressed; this goal demonstrates the changing nature of ocean governance and perhaps international relations as a whole. Here, the common-pool nature of the World Ocean and the linking of security to these resources highlight the interdependence not only of ecosystems but also of people and nations. This marks a change in the way that some international relations scholars see the world. Where the world was once predominately seen as a set of individual and self-serving nations, there is increasing evidence that individual military security comes up short compared to collective and comprehensive models of security that envision an increased role for regional navies, the protection of common-pool resources, and greater cooperation in general.

Two of the reasons for classifying ecological values under security policy, as discussed in chapter 3, affect the context of the rest of the book. The first reason is that many theorists and historians note that countries will readily go to war or use state-sanctioned violence to control scarce resources. This "resource wars" thesis is explored in detail. The second reason ecological protection and management is categorized as a security goal is that human action and some natural phenomena can create direct ecological problems of survival for nations and their people. The most poignant example is the threat that small island nations face from rising sea levels, which are said to result from human-induced global warming. In this case, managing human impacts and caring for the environment are ways to implement ecological security policies. Finally, chapter 3 explains how the Law of the Sea and the Fishery Stock Agreement fit into ocean security schemes. The chapter's conclusion suggests that the most con-temporary thinking on ocean security finds the controversies sur-rounding ecological systems to be of vital importance. In short, the survival and well-being of human and other species noted in chapter 3 depend on the successful governance of many of the ocean controversies that are discussed in chapter 2.

Chapter 4 offers a chronology of important ocean dates and events, such as the beginning of life on Earth, the start of scien-tific marine inquiry, and some key moments in modern marine diplomacy. Chapter 5 provides brief sketches of a number of important people and events in the field, including Capt. Jacques Cousteau, Sylvia Earle, and Arvid Pardoe, as well as the creation of the Incidents at Sea Treaty and the *Torrey Canyon* oil spill. Chapter 6 provides important data such as a list of nations and their coastal assets, threatened marine mammal populations, world fishing data, and information on the condition of coastal environments as measured by the extent of mangroves, coral reefs, and sea grasses. Chapter 7 presents sections from interna-tional ocean documents, including the Law of the Sea, the Fishery Stock Agreement, and Chapter 17 of Agenda 21, an agreement that came out of the Rio Conference on Environment and Development in 1992 and set important goals for "the oceans and all kinds of seas." Chapter 8 provides a directory of ocean-related organizations, including U.S. organizations, inter-national nongovernmental organizations (INGOs), research institutes, and international governmental organizations. The final chapter catalogs numerous print and nonprint resources that will help beginning researchers find more information about ocean politics. This chapter includes scientific databases, Internet resources, and reference books that will give users up-to-date information on the state of ocean affairs.

References

Haas, Ernst. 1982. "Words Can Hurt You: Or, Who Said What to Whom about Regimes." In Stephen D. Krasner, ed., *International Regimes*. Ithaca, NY: Cornell University Press.

Hardin, Garret. 1968. "The Tragedy of the Commons." *Science* 162: 1243–1248.

Jasonoff, Sheila. 1998. "Skinning Scientific Cats." In Ken Conca and Geoffrey Dabelko, eds., *Green Planet Blues*. Boulder, CO: Westview Press.

Juda, Lawrence. 1996. *International Law and Ocean Use Management: The Evolution of Ocean Governance*. New York: Routledge.

Reuter, Paul. 1989. *Introduction to the Law of Treaties*. New York: Pinter Publishers.

Smith, Zachary. 2001. *Environmental Policy Paradox*, 3rd ed. Englewood Cliffs, NJ: Prentice-Hall.

Victor, David, Kal Raustiala, and Eugene Skolnikoff, eds. 1998. *The Implementation and Effectiveness of International Environmental Commitments: Theory and Practice*. Cambridge, MA: MIT Press.

Wapner, Paul. 1996. *Environmental Activism and World Civic Politics*. Albany: State University of New York Press.

Wood, Richard, Anne Keen, John Mitchell, and Jonathan Gregory. 1999. "Changing Spatial Structure of the Thermohaline Circulation in Response to Atmospheric CO_2 Forcing in a Climate Model." *Nature* 399: 572–576.

2

Making Waves: Problems, Controversies, and Solutions

This chapter will cover a number of topics that are important to ocean management: integrated coastal management (ICM), fishing, whaling, pollution, mining, and jurisdictional disputes. The pollution section includes a case study of the *Exxon Valdez* oil spill of 1989. At the conclusion of the chapter, some policy suggestions for the future will be offered.

Integrated Coastal Management

Some of the world's most important resources exist where the ocean meets the land. This terrain, the coast, contains wetlands, reefs, beaches, and other sensitive areas. The best management of these areas proceeds from a holistic approach that recognizes each part of the coast as an important component of a larger ecosystem. To work with coastal systems holistically, coastal management must be integrated, or organized, at two levels: ecological and governmental. This effort is called integrated coastal management.

In ecologically integrated coastal management, coastal areas are thought of as larger systems instead of separate land and water environments. Moreover, each part of the whole is recognized as important and dependent on the rest of the system; every part mutually influences other components of the system. Thus, for example, the health of coral reefs can influence the health of fish populations and the beachfront, and the beachfront in turn can influence the health of the coastal vegetation. Coming full circle, then, the status of reefs can have an indirect or even a direct influence on that of coastal vegetation. Conversely, the flow of pollutants from the inland may harm those same reefs and adversely affect fish populations and coastal vegetation, and any storm protection offered by these reefs may be diminished. Ecologically integrated coastal management understands these systemic connections and places a value on the health of all components.

Ecologically focused coastal management strives primarily for the ideal of *sustainable development.* According to this ideal, natural resource use today should not compromise the same use for future generations. Sustainable development is achieved by insulating the system and its parts from disruptions, most of which are caused by human activity. For this reason, ICM is most important for coastal areas that have high levels of human use, occupation, or exploitation. Insulating the system from disruptions is accomplished by mitigating or limiting human uses that cause problems for the area. ICM responds to the demand for sustainable development within and through government agencies.

Governmentally integrated coastal management strives primarily for collaboration between agencies, for many different arms of the government have responsibility for managing coastal regions. Even if the ICM policies recognize the coast as a larger ecological system, efforts to work with this ecosystem may be frustrated if the various government agencies are working separately. Typically, for instance, inland pollution control is managed by one government agency, fishing is managed by another, and mineral exploitation is handled by an altogether different agency. Governmentally integrated coastal management works to draw these concerns together through agency collaboration.

Agency collaboration is a complicated endeavor because the "personalities" and organizational cultures of all the agencies must be accommodated. One difficulty that arises when government agencies work together is that the different entities may not want to share resources or credit because they may view each other as competitors. However, all agencies do not have the capacity or ability to work expertly with coastal areas. This is especially true for organizations that usually do not deal with the oceans but find themselves working on a particular coastal project that demands their expertise. For example, transportation departments may not be familiar with beach erosion, but they may have to build a road or a trail around fragile littoral (coastal/shore) zones. If an integrated approach is employed, the expertise of road engineers from other more knowledgeable agencies can be called on so that the road can be built without damaging the beach. Thus, governmentally integrated coastal management can be complicated, and the collaboration of agencies may be necessary.

In the United States, legislation that encourages integrated approaches to coastal management dates back to the early 1970s and is growing in popularity today. The United States was the first nation to adopt ICM, through the Coastal Zone Management Act of 1972 (CZMA). The CZMA places the first 3 miles of ocean within the jurisdiction of the state, but the remaining area is to be managed by a variety of federal agencies, such as the Departments of Defense, Commerce, Agriculture, Interior, Transportation, and Energy. More recently, ICM received further endorsement by the Oceans Act of 2000, which was signed into law by President Bill Clinton's administration. This act is intended to create a unified ocean and coastal policy, as advised by the new National Oceans Commission. This commission is made up of business, environmental, science, and government groups, all of which are important stakeholders (parties interested in the outcomes of a policy) in ocean management.

In conclusion, good coastal management is integrated ecologically and governmentally. Both dimensions are important. Understanding the coast as a larger ecosystem informs policies that place a value on a healthy, holistic environment. Government is responsible for limiting the effect that humans have on this larger coastal ecosystem. The level of success that a coastal management regime enjoys may be a function of how well these two essential components are implemented together.

Fishing

Fishing is one of the most important uses of the ocean. This section will discuss how and why fish and fishing are important; in addition, some of the concepts and problems of fishery conservation will be addressed, and there will be a brief overview of the operation of national and international fishing regimes.

The Importance of Fish and the Effects of Fishing

Second only to navigation, fishing is the primary human use of the World Ocean. Commercial and small-scale fishing supports about 200 million people in direct employment. Another 500 million draw their livelihoods indirectly from marine resources (Wells and Gawler 1999, 118). An area in the ocean that is used for fishing is called a "fishery," and such areas usually have populations of specific fish. Fish account for 16 percent of all animal protein intake in the world, and they may account for 40 percent or more in developing nations, in Japan, and in Norway (Frankel 1995, 17).

However, fisheries are in danger. The world fish catch nearly doubled over a twenty-year period, from 50 million tons in 1975 to 95 million tons in 1995. Consequently, the United Nations Environment Programme (UNEP) reported that "repeated failures to implement measures to control over-fishing mean that approximately 60 percent of the world's ocean fisheries are now at or near the point at which yields decline" (UNEP 2000, 45). In other words, most of the world's fisheries are being exploited faster than they can recover. Fisheries are becoming depleted as a result of overfishing.

Overfishing does not indiscriminately affect fishing populations. Food chains become worn down one predator species at a time, leaving the ecosystem with "junk" species and a drop in biodiversity and biointegrity. Biodiversity relates to the amount of different species within an area. Biointegrity involves the strength of an ecosystem in terms of resisting disease, species extinction, and other ecological infirmities. In the Black Sea, for example, populations of jellyfish have increased dramatically as their economically important competitors have been removed. This situation has reduced the number of major fisheries in the Black Sea from twenty-six to five (Williams 1998).

Although specific fish are diminished purposefully, other marine life is diminished indiscriminately. Fishing nets can extend for miles, catching species that are not targeted and even species that may be protected. This "by-catch" is a serious problem for fish populations. By-catching wastes about 27 million metric tons (59,523 million pounds) of fish annually, almost one-third of the total annual world fish catch. When by-catch is added to the world fish catch, the total burden on world fisheries can be as high as 120 million metric tons (265,440 million pounds) per year (Hyvarinen, Wall, and Lutchman 1998). In addition, 1.5 million dolphin and small whales are killed each year as by-catch and by pollution and target hunts (Frankel 1995, 29). These figures indicate not only a tremendous waste but also an unnecessary disruption in the world food chain and a threat to ecological stability and security.

In sum, fishing is a vital aspect of the world's diet, economy, and biodiversity. However, overwhelming evidence shows that these crucial uses of the marine world are in danger. As Nigel Williams (1998, 809) observed, "Present fishing policy is unsustainable. The food-web structure is changing. . . . At least 60% of the world's 200 most commercially valuable species are overfished or fished to the limit." If fishing is to continue to be a thriving part of all these systems (dietary, economic, and ecological), it is critical that we understand the causes of overfishing. Several factors that contribute to this problem will be discussed in the following section.

Principles and Problems of Fishery Conservation

The tools and policies that national and international governments have used to regulate the fishing industry have largely been inadequate (Juda 1996; Cicin-Sain and Knecht 1998). This section will explore the reasons why fishery conservation is riddled with problems. In large part, fisheries are allowed to become depleted due to overcapitalization, open-access fishing regimes, and poor use of knowledge about fisheries.

Perhaps one of the core causes of overfishing is the problem of open access, which is also discussed in chapter 1. In an open-access regime, anyone can use a fishery. In the spirit of the freedom of the seas doctrine, users are often not limited to any specific area, and they are permitted to take as much fish as they can get on board their boat. Consequently, new fishing boats entering an existing, developed fishery start to compete against all the other fishing boats and crews already there. The number of available fish, however, does not increase along with the added boats, which means that more boats are vying for the same fish. To become more competitive against those other boats, fishing fleets have an incentive to invest in more efficient ways of getting the greatest amount of fish possible. This practice is called "overcapitalization."

Overcapitalization in fishing gear and boats is one reason why fisheries are unstable. Overcapitalization encourages more and more boats with better equipment to pursue fewer and fewer fish as fishing fleets compete with each other over the same dwindling fish stocks. To succeed in catching large quantities of these fish, fleets have been forced not only to add more boats but also to have the latest, best gear (such as sonar systems and refrigeration) in order to remain competitive. As a result, fishing fleets have become brutally efficient at getting the most fish for their investment dollars.

Overfishing is also caused by inadequate knowledge about fish populations, health, and sustainability, as well as improper use of existing knowledge. Given the nature of the resource, fishing policy is forced to estimate fish stocks through projections. These projections are based on how many fish are being caught over a period of time and the amount of effort required to land that number of fish. In other words, if 2 tons of fish were caught in a day using basic fishing gear but it took more time or more sophisticated gear to catch the same amount six months later, the fish population is presumed to have diminished.

This projection method also relies on the precarious assumption that protective restrictions on fishing will occur when policymakers realize that the fish are becoming scarce, as indicated by decreased fish catches per unit of effort exerted. However, scientific fish population models often err in the direction of systematically overestimating the number of fish, which then justifies high harvest rates and fewer restrictions (Wilder 1998).

In addition, population estimates differ from study to study. Because fish often travel great distances, results are easily skewed: the fish may be missed in one study but double-counted in another. Thus, with multiple results, the numbers that are endorsed in the management regime may have more to do with the political demands of industry rather than the true conditions of the fishery.

Yet, even when there is continued evidence for declining stocks, fishing fleets have historically become more sophisticated and efficient to keep their catches high. In fact, they have become efficient enough to actually increase the global fish catch, thereby deceptively reducing the urgency of the need to protect fish and their habitats. Global fish catches are now declining from the peaks reached in the mid-1990s, and managers and biologists will have to work on recovering crippled life at sea.

U.S. Domestic Fishery Management

Fishery management in the United States is not immune from the problems just mentioned. Current U.S. domestic fishing policy is codified in the Sustainable Fisheries Act of 1996 (SFA) and the Oceans Act of 2000. Although the names of the management schemes change over time, some components remain consistent through the years, including the demands for maximum yield, regional control, and indirect regulation of the fishing industry.

Maximum yield, sometimes called "maximum sustainable yield," is a consistent theme in nearly all national and international fishery management schemes. Like sustainable development, maximum sustainable yield is an ideal. The goal is to regulate fishing so that the greatest amount of fish are taken from a fishery without impairing its ability to continue to produce desirable fish. Power is lent to the idea of maximum yield by a fear that "surplus" fish (those not needed for breeding) are wasted if they are not caught for human use. But ecologists point out that fish, like all other parts of the world ecosystem, fulfill the ecological functions of an area even if they are not used by humans. In this way, fish can never be wasted by not catching them, though it has already been shown that a great many fish are wasted *after* they are caught.

One problem with maximum yield management plans, as discussed in the previous section, is that marine biologists may overestimate fish populations. Accordingly, managers often do not have a good understanding of the actual amount of fish in the fishery and thus cannot make a sound judgment on how much of that population should be considered surplus and available to the fishing industry. Political pressures exerted on managers by industry usually foster a liberal interpretation of what a maximum yield should be, in order to enhance economic benefits.

Regional control is another consistent theme in U.S. domestic fishing management. Federal commercial fishing regimes allow for federal control, but typically, control is systematically delegated to regional councils that allow for significant industry input. Consequently, some regions are more permissive than others. Regional fishing management in a given location is usually guided by a council that oversees the fisheries within that geographic area. These councils are subject to pressures from industry, whose primary interest is landing more fish. If the regional councils fail to control overfishing, they may lose control of the process to the federal government—but not before many warnings have been issued and a great deal of time has passed. Since the federal response to this problem is reactive, federal intervention in U.S. fisheries only becomes a reality after those fisheries are already in trouble.

Indirect management, another consistent component of the domestic regulation of the fishing industry, has done little to curb the basic problems of overfishing. For example, overcapitalization has been allowed to flourish. When the issue was presented to the administration of President Ronald Reagan, the idea of added regulations for the fishing industry was said to conflict with "basic economic liberties" (Hsu and Wilen 1997, 804). If the growth of the fishing industry is not within the scope of fishery management, policy is forced to depend on indirect measures, such as fishing seasons.

Unfortunately, "short seasons govern even those [fisheries] in good shape biologically, leading to relatively poorer quality fish, and encouraging fishing with methods that emphasize volume and induce by-catch, discarding, and other forms of waste" (Hsu and Wilen 1997, 804). Management that focuses on seasons actually gives an incentive to the fishing industry to increase its investment in its fleets, since there is less time to get the same amount of fish. The fishing fleet that is best equipped to land the most fish in a short amount of time "wins," and the fishery still becomes overfished.

International Fishery Management

Some 47 to 50 percent of the world's fisheries are fully exploited, leaving no room for further increases in catch without depleting future fish generations. Another 15 to 18 percent are already overexploited, and 9 to 10 percent of the world's fisheries are either depleted or recovering from depletion. Thus, in total, 71 to 78 percent of the world's fisheries are already threatened or are on the brink of being threatened with severe problems, which include biodiversity loss, economic catastrophe, and food insecurity (United Nations Food and Agricultural Organization 2000). (Food insecurity is not having enough food for a population dependent on a specific source, such as fish. People in many poor nations use fish as their primary source of protein.) This trend began in the 1950s when the world fish catch increased about 6 percent every year for twenty years. In the 1970s and 1980s, observable declines emerged, and today, global fisheries are in

serious trouble. The global declines are caused by the same factors involved in the national and regional declines in fish catches,
with overfishing bearing the bulk of the responsibility. However,
international fisheries have been even more difficult to manage
due to the doctrine of mare liberum.

Prior to the Law of the Sea, countries could only protect their
fisheries within their 3-mile territorial limits, but with the advent
of the exclusive economic zone (see the "Jurisdictions and
Disputes" section later in this chapter), coastal nations can now
manage 200 miles of ocean. Because most fish are found within
200 miles of the shore, approximately 90 percent of the global fish
and shellfish catches are now under the control of coastal nations
(Schurman 1998, 107; Vallega 2001). Outside the EEZs, international regulatory management has been largely nonexistent,
though the United Nations Food and Agriculture Organization
(FAO) does have a regional program, and starting in 2002, the
Fishery Stock Agreement began providing for more governance
on the high seas. In the next paragraphs, the FAO program and
the FSA will be explained in greater detail.

The FAO's Regional Fisheries Bodies Program does not provide global fishery rules. Rather, it establishes a framework in
which regional fisheries can work together to manage the fishing
in specific areas. These regional bodies determine what species
will be protected, what fishing seasons and areas will be set up,
and what gear and fishing methods will be prohibited.

Fishery management organized under the FAO may incorporate various regional approaches, but the primary goal for the
FAO is fishery security—the insurance that fisheries will remain
plentiful, thus protecting the communities and people that
depend on fishing. The FAO is particularly interested in fish in
terms of food security. Food security is about making sure people
have enough to eat, and using fish as food security means ensuring that there are enough fish to supply that need. Since most
fisheries in the world are at the point of decline, the FAO has
good reason to be alarmed at the potential for food insecurity.

The FSA represents a radical turn for ocean management and
politics because it allows one state to interfere with the fishing
vessels of another state, a situation that was avoided in the past
due to the potential for sparking a military conflict. (Much about
the FSA is discussed in chapter 3, which deals with ocean security; the agreement is designed to prevent both mismanagement
and military conflicts regarding international fishing.) Beyond
that, the FSA avoids the "flags of convenience problem," which

essentially relates to the act of obtaining and flying under the flag of a more permissive country (see the related discussion later in this chapter). Under the FSA, if a regional fishery is in decline, a regional organization is put together to represent both regional and interested nonregional countries. This organization can make rules regarding access to and use of the fishery. Similar regional organizations have existed for years, but they have suffered from a lack of authority, and fishing vessels flagged under states that were not part of the regional organizations did not have to observe these rules. Under the FSA, however, regional fishery organizations can board boats of fishing fleets that belong to nations not willing to observe the conservation rules, and they can deny them access to the fishery.

Still, the FSA only applies to migratory or straddling fish stocks, which are stocks that move through or between national jurisdictions. Fish stocks that do not migrate or straddle national boundaries and are solely confined to high-seas fisheries are not covered under this agreement (though nearly all fish species have some connection to coastal ecosystems). Also, the FSA does not limit capitalization in fishing fleets, and it relies on the same uncertain projections of sustainable yield that nearly all national and international fishery management uses.

In conclusion, fisheries have been in jeopardy in recent decades largely as a result of free, open seas and a lack of organized conservation. If these fisheries are to recover from a tragedy of the commons (see chapter 1), national and international policies will have to acknowledge and enforce fair limits on human endeavor. Since the FSA is only now being tested, it will take some time to assess its effectiveness.

Whaling

Whaling is a controversial issue because some nations have a historical and economic reliance on whaling and whale products whereas others have embraced the whale as an environmental icon to be protected. Currently, a moratorium on all commercial whaling is in place. However, the struggle over this issue is not settled because whaling nations want to resume commercial hunting. This section will cover the significant history of whaling, the tools and exceptions that are used to manage whaling, and the revised management procedure that may be employed to reinstate commercial whaling at some point in the future.

Whaling is managed by the International Whaling Commission (IWC). The IWC was created in 1946 by the International Convention for the Regulation of Whaling. The convention was originally thought of as a fishery agreement that would essentially manage itself by setting total allowable catch (TAC) limits. Global limits were necessary because whales migrate great distances and are a common-pool resource that is vulnerable to overharvesting by one or more nations at the expense of others.

According to the IWC (2001), "the purpose of the Convention is to provide for the proper conservation of whale stocks and thus make possible the orderly development of the whaling industry." This goal has remained the same over time, but the way it is implemented has changed. At the start of the convention, the IWC enacted a plan to simply reduce whaling in order to make it sustainable. However, in 1982, enough nonwhaling nations had entered into the convention that all commercial whaling was "paused."

This moratorium on commercial whaling is, according to the IWC, a temporary management plan to allow whale stocks to recover from overharvesting. Nonwhaling nations have installed the moratorium on commercial whaling by becoming members in the IWC and voting to end the practice. At the beginning of the IWC, only twelve nations were members, and they all hunted whales. By the 1982 moratorium, however, the membership stood at over forty, with most being nations that did not hunt whales. Since each country has a single vote in the IWC, the whaling nations were easily outnumbered in their own organization, and they lost control of the management plan. Nonwhaling nations joined the International Whaling Commission under the influence of environmental nongovernmental organizations.

NGOs, including groups such as Greenpeace and the Sea Shepherd Conservation Society, are often credited with pushing nonwhaling states to end the practice of whaling. And since those nations did not have economies or constituencies that depended on whaling, they did not have much to lose when NGOs asked them to join the IWC. NGOs have even been known to pay delegations to attend the IWC's annual meetings. Thus, NGOs and NGO members have played a large role in ending commercial whaling. This is one example of the way in which citizens at the local level who are a part of an NGO can affect global politics and ocean management.

The IWC has been recognized as a very successful international regime because its member nations do not violate the whaling convention's agreement. Further, the IWC has implemented the plan it agreed to when the moratorium was placed on commercial whaling. One reason the organization has been successful is because it has defined the scope of international whale management as truly global. Thus, unlike many other international ocean agreements, IWC regulations pertain to "all waters in which whaling is prosecuted," including waters in the territorial seas (Birnie 1996, 52). Since whales are protected in all ocean waters, one nation is not permitted to spoil the efforts of the rest by hunting the animals as they pass along its sovereign coastline. If the territorial seas were exempted from the IWC rules, conservation of the species would suffer and there would be an incentive for each nation to rush to harvest as many whales as possible in its own waters before the animals passed into another nation's territory. Consequently, whale management in *all* waters is an important factor in the success of the IWC.

There are two exceptions to the moratorium on commercial whaling: scientific hunting and aboriginal hunting. A permit for scientific hunting is issued by the state of an expedition's flagship, and prior approval from the IWC is not required. But a minority of states, among them Japan, have been accused of using scientific research as a facade for commercial whale hunting. As Patricia Birnie (1996, 66) noted, "This loophole had recently been abused by states to keep a minimal industry alive in the face of the current moratorium on whaling." Inherent in the moratorium is the expectation that scientific expeditions will use the carcasses in some manner so the whales are not wasted, and commercial "disposal" (that is, selling of whale products) is allowed. However, whaling ships have been known to waste up to 90 percent of a carcass and dispose of this portion at sea to make room onboard for more whales. Currently, Japan kills over four hundred minke whales per year. Minke whale meat can bring as much as U.S.$90 per pound in Japan, where it is used for sashimi.

The second exception to the moratorium is for aboriginal hunting, which allows for limited, subsistence-based hunting by indigenous peoples recognized by the IWC. An exception of this type must be approved by the IWC prior to the taking of the whales, and it is subject to an algorithmic formula that considers the available whale stock in determining how many whaling tribes can be permitted to hunt (Givens 1999). Indigenous peoples have fought hard to pursue their traditional practice by lobbying governments and participating in national delegations to the IWC, but aboriginal whale hunts are heavily protested by environmental activists. One group that has been at the forefront of the whaling issue is the Sea Shepherd Conservation Society. The society believes that no exceptions to the moratorium should be allowed. For their part, indigenous people argue that the hunts are a vital part of their history, livelihood, and cultural heritage. Ending these hunts, they say, would damage a significant aspect of their cultural existence. This claim is supported by the experience of the Makaw people: by the time they were permitted to resume whale hunting, no living Makaw had ever hunted a whale or even knew how to do so.

Infractions of the IWC agreement are relatively rare, but whaling nations are attempting to reinstate commercial whaling under the revised management plan. This plan takes a scientific wildlife management approach to whaling. According to the plan, strict limits will be observed by whalers, who will agree not to take more than a certain percentage of the estimated population of a given species. Because the estimates are not very accurate, the plan uses assumptions of low whale populations to ensure a more confident guess about whale numbers.

This plan was approved by a scientific committee and by the larger IWC in 1994. However, environmentalists say that it is based on the desire for profit and that whaling itself is the cruel and unnecessary killing of another sentient (feeling) being. In fact, the Sea Shepherd Conservation Society, which advocates this view, is blamed for sinking nine Norwegian whaling vessels because Norway continues to kill over seven hundred minke whales per year (Andresen 1998, 432; "So Much for Saving" 2000). Nonetheless, in the 2000 meeting of the IWC, the group agreed to expedite the implementation of the revised management plan, and it has slated that goal as a priority for future meetings.

There are two reasons why the revised management plan has recently become a tangible option for the IWC. First, Japan has made alliances with some cash-poor island nations. These nations, which include Saint Lucia, Dominica, and other eastern Caribbean nations, are suspected of selling their votes in the IWC for large amounts of money. Although none of these countries has a whaling industry, they regularly vote in line with Japan, which gives them a great deal of financial support as well (Prideaux 2000). Second, the North Atlantic whaling states have created their own international whaling regime, which threatens to resume whaling if the revised management plan is not implemented. The North

Atlantic Marine Mammals Commission (NAMMCO) was established in 1992 and includes Norway, Iceland, Greenland, and the Faroe Islands. Japan, Mexico, Russia, Ireland, and South Africa are sympathetic to NAMMCO's goal of reclaiming commercial whaling under scientific wildlife management models. The existence of NAMMCO is a powerful incentive for the IWC to implement the revised management plan because the IWC depends on the whaling nations to voluntarily honor the moratorium. If the whaling nations chose to ignore the IWC, the moratorium would become irrelevant, since nonwhaling nations already observe the moratorium by default.

Thus, whaling conservation has had a history of unexpected turns, and the complex issues it entails have not been resolved. Indeed, some challenges to the NGOs and nonwhaling states are well organized and gaining momentum. If the IWC continues to maintain a hard line on the whaling moratorium, the organization may be abandoned by the whaling nations—the only nations that really matter when it comes to regulation. However, if the IWC decides to adopt the revised management plan, nonwhaling member states will face a powerful backlash from environmental groups that have successfully made the whale an emblem for environmental protection.

Sea-Level Rise

The sea has been rising at about 2 millimeters (.078 inches) per year since the mid-1800s, meaning that, on average, it has risen as much as 20 centimeters (7.8 inches) over roughly a century and a half (Douglas, Kearney, and Leatherman 2001). Although this is a small increase compared to the 120-meter (about 394-foot) sea-level rise that occurred during the warming period after the last Ice Age 21,000 years ago, scientists are concerned about the rising levels for several reasons.

For one thing, they are the most positive indicator of global warming that we have (Douglas, Kearney, and Leatherman 2001). During the past 100 years, the sea-level rise has increased at ten times its previous rate. Over the same period, the mean global temperature has risen over .5°C (1°F), and it is projected to continue to increase by another 1.4 to 5.8°C (2.5 to 10.4°F) in the next 100 years. As the earth warms, freshwater frozen in glaciers melts, and the volume of the ocean increases, thus rising in level. This phenomenon is already occurring at an increasing pace. Glaciers and ice sheets are melting, and the polar regions are warming. The Greenland ice sheet alone is losing about 51 cubic *kilometers* (41,346,132 acre-feet or 13,472,774,470,954 gallons) of ice each year, which is sufficient to raise the sea level .13 millimeters (.005 inches) a year (Krabil et al. 2000). This increase in sea volume can continue for a very long time, since nearly all freshwater found on the planet is frozen in ice sheets, glaciers, and ice caps. Of course, about 97 percent of the world's water is already in the ocean, but of the remaining 3 percent (the only freshwater on the planet), 2.997 percent is frozen in glaciers and in the polar ice caps.

An even more dramatic reason to be concerned about this problem is that the polar ice sheets are destabilizing. In 2002, a piece of the Antarctic ice sheet the size of Connecticut broke off. Scientists estimate that should either of Antarctica's vast west or east ice sheets collapse, sea levels would rise as much as 20 and 200 feet, respectively ("Antarctica Key" 2002). Keeping in mind that for every degree of sea-level rise that occurs the landward loss can be fifty to one hundred times as great, the amount of land submerged under these projections would be catastrophic.

Without ice sheet collapse, the sea level may rise as much as 1 meter (3.28 feet) in the next 100 years, putting small islands such as Tuvalu in the South Pacific on alert that their countries will disappear in about fifty years. Similarly, the thousands of islands that constitute the Maldives nation are typically at 1 to 1.5 meters (3.28 to 4.92 feet) above sea level, so a 1-meter (3.28-foot) rise would essentially wipe out this country as well. Also affected would be coastal-dwelling people on continental landmasses, particularly those who live at river deltas. Over 100 million people would be displaced in China, Bangladesh, Egypt, and Nigeria alone under current projections for sea-level rise in the next 100 years.

Other problems related to a rising sea level concern scientists. One prominent issue is beach erosion. In fact, about 70 percent of the world's beaches are eroding, and rising sea levels are an underlying cause. For sandy tourist locations, the loss of beach is an expensive proposition, as it can cost billions of dollars to replenish vanishing sand—which, in the end, is a futile game against the march of tides. Beaches lose their soil and sand as a result of submergence and longshore transport through waves and currents. Also, coastal marshes and upland agriculture and flora and fauna can be displaced as the saline water and saline-tolerant plant species take over freshwater agricultural areas. In addition, as saltwater advances landward, it penetrates freshwater aquifers, killing trees and other plants and making the freshwater unusable to humans without significant and expensive treatment. Most coastal areas are already experiencing some degree of saltwater intrusion as a combined result of the overdrafting of aquifers (too many wells) and advancing sea levels.

Politically, sea-level rise is part of the global-warming debate that tends to pit wealthy, industrialized countries, which emit the vast majority of greenhouse gases, against poor, less industrialized countries. The reason for this is that wealthy nations see poor but heavily populated countries as having the potential to warm the planet more than anyone else given their potential for industrialization. In addition, some industrialized countries, notably the United States, have said that, as an issue of fairness, they would not agree to the Kyoto Protocol, which sets emission standards to 1990 levels, as long as it treats them differently from less industrialized countries. Meanwhile, less industrialized countries argue that if their ability to emit gases that come from hydrocarbons is limited, they will never be able to enjoy the same degree of wealth and modernized development that industrialized countries take for granted. In addition, less industrialized countries contend that much of the emissions put out by industrialized countries is a by-product of the production of luxury goods, not essentials. They also argue that the amount of emissions the atmosphere can handle, whatever that might be, should be divided equally among humanity so that survival emissions (such as those produced by cooking and by heating homes) could be accommodated. Consequently, threats from global warming, sea-level rise, and related problems (for example, biodiversity loss) rest in the balance of global hydrocarbon energy distribution. Currently, wealthy countries control this distribution.

In 1992, the United Nations Framework Convention on Climate Change (UNFCCC) was negotiated, and it went into effect one year later. Under this regime, nations were directed to come up with a plan to reduce global emissions that included a voluntary reduction of emissions to 1990 levels for industrial nations. In 1997, the Kyoto Protocol, a part of the UNFCCC, mandated industrialized countries to reduce emissions from the 1990 levels (lower standards were set for less industrialized countries). For example, the United States would have to have 7 percent fewer emissions than in 1990 according to the protocol. However, as mentioned in the first chapter of this book, the United States has since rejected this plan.

Were the plan to go into effect, it would still assume a global temperature increase of over 1°C (around 2°F). But without the limits set in the protocol, the globe may warm an additional 6°C or more (over 10°F). It is possible that this kind of dramatic increase in global mean temperature would result in the ice sheet collapses mentioned earlier and severe changes in weather patterns, such as floods, mud slides, and droughts of epic proportions.

With only a .5°C (.9°F) increase around the world, some catastrophic changes have already occurred. The colder regions of the world seem to have responded with rapid temperature increases. Antarctica is reporting a 2.7°C (5°F) increase. Alaska is reporting a 3.8°C (7°F) increase, and at the same time, a large peninsula has lost 4 million acres of pine forest to a beetle that is thought to have doubled its reproductive ability in the warmer seasons. This is the largest forest killed by a bug in North American history, and the lead botanist studying the phenomenon has said it may be one of the first directly observable effects of global warming (Egan 2002). It is plausible that the effects of a single degree of warming have been disastrous; an increase five times greater than that may well be cataclysmic.

In conclusion, sea-level rise and global warming are very serious threats. Over 100 million coastal residents, thousands of islands and atolls (very small islands), agriculture, and tourist locations face a threat to their survival. Within this context, global warming can rightfully be considered an ecological security risk (see chapter 3).

Pollution

Marine pollution did not become a global concern until the 1960s, and significant marine pollution agreements were not seen until the late 1960s and 1970s. Even in the short time since, however, much has happened to help us understand global marine pollution and its management. This section will discuss some of the different types of ocean pollution, as well as the Regional Seas Programme that has been developed under the United Nations Environment Programme. Special attention will be given to oil pollution, and the section will conclude with a case study of the *Exxon Valdez* oil spill.

Most marine pollution starts on land and is due to human activities. In fact, over 70 percent of marine pollution comes from land-based sources, and the dumping of pollutants into the ocean and marine transportation make up another 20 percent of all international ocean pollution (Cicin-Sain and Knecht 1998, 38; Wilder 1998; United Nations Division for Sustainable Development 1999). Inland pollution includes sewage, trace metals, chemical waste, oil spills, and other toxins that do immeasurable damage to coastal ecosystems. Fish are particularly affected by inland pollution because, as studies have shown, "approximately 85 percent of commercially harvested fish depend on estuaries and near coastal waters at some stage in their life cycle" (National Research Council 1997, 18). If these waters are polluted, contaminants can have a direct effect on the reproduction and development of the fish that use them.

Chlorinated pesticides such as PCBs, dioxins, and DDT are of particular concern because these chemicals are "persistent," meaning they accumulate and remain in the body. For marine mammals such as seals and porpoises that eat fish contaminated with these pollutants, the toxins become a permanent part of their fatty tissue. Humans who eat these fish (or mammals) also accumulate this poison in their bodies. Moreover, this poisoning has been linked to cancer. Rachel Carson's famous book, *Silent Spring*, brought attention to this problem in the 1960s regarding DDT. The use of DDT was eventually banned in the United States, but U.S. chemical companies still produce the toxin and export it to other countries.

Another major pollution concern is sewage. When treatment for human sewage is not available, this waste often ends up in the ocean. Several human problems emerge from the contamination of marine areas with sewage. For example, direct human exposure, which is typically experienced by ocean bathers, can cause illness. One in twenty people entering seawater classified as "acceptable" under some of the most strict water quality standards in the United States and the European Union will become ill even after just one swim. Some 250 million cases of gastroenteritis and upper respiratory disease occur every year from this kind of direct exposure to sewage. For nations that lack adequate sewage treatment, whether for lack of money or for other political reasons, this risk is assumed to be much worse.

Indirect exposure via eating contaminated shellfish is an even more serious problem. During a continent-wide outbreak of illness traced to contaminated shellfish that began in Peru and plagued Latin America from 1991 to 1995, 10,000 people died from pollution-caused disease. Of diseases related to food, the total amount caused by sewage-contaminated shellfish is 11 percent in the United States, 20 percent in Australia, and 70 percent in Japan (GESAMP 2001). Infectious hepatitis, a serious disease that can result from exposure to contaminated shellfish, is typically responsible for 2.5 million cases of illness per year, resulting in about 25,000 deaths and 25,000 cases of long-term disability. Other diseases that can be contracted from exposure to contaminated shellfish include (but are not limited to) leprosy, Japanese encephalitis, dengue fever, and diphtheria (GESAMP 2001).

Recently, air pollution from ships has also become a concern. The International Maritime Organization (IMO) has approved limits to ship emissions, but they will be phased in gradually. Furthermore, recently enacted air pollution restrictions will only apply to new ships or ships undergoing major conversions, and they will only reduce emissions by 1 percent per year. Meanwhile, "ship engines produce some of the highest amounts of pollution of all combustion sources per ton of fuel consumed" (Corbett and Fischbeck 1997, 823). The hard fact is that ships produce the same amount of nitrogen emissions as all U.S. automobiles combined. Also, they emit half as much sulfur as all U.S. sulfur emissions and account for 16 percent of all petroleum sulfur emissions worldwide (Corbett and Fischbeck 1997). Consequently, air pollution from ships would be a good subject for future research and policy work.

Finally, the problem of eutrophication is now recognized as a significant threat to marine species. Eutrophication is the oversupply of organic material to an ecosystem, which may cause an increase in algae. An excessive amount of algae can be harmful, especially if the algae is toxic to begin with, because the algae blooms (or overpopulates) in an ocean space. An overabundance of algae at the top of the sea layer prevents light and nutrients from passing through the water, and dying algae float to the bottom of the area and release the carbon they have stored from photosynthesis. The net result is that oxygen becomes depleted, and other species in the area die. The health effects of harmful algae blooms on humans can be quite serious as well and include cholera and other diseases.

Eutrophication can occur as a result of sewage pollution, loss of wetlands, global warming, and the overharvesting of fish. However, it is often directly related to the amount of agricultural fertilizers and nitrates used near rivers that empty into the ocean. The increased use of agricultural fertilizers corresponds with the number of algal blooms experienced each year. In the early 1970s,

just over 90 million tons of agricultural fertilizer was used globally, but by the mid-1990s (with the greatest use actually occurring
in the late 1980s), the global use of agricultural fertilizer was over
130 million tons a year (a 30 percent increase). At the same time,
the number of harmful algae blooms has risen across the globe.

For example, as a result of agricultural fertilizer runoff in the
Midwest, which leaches as nonpoint source pollution into the
Mississippi River, there is a "dead zone" in the Gulf of Mexico at
the mouth of the river. A dead zone is typically a spot in the ocean
that has experienced eutrophication resulting in the loss of most
of the oxygen; the zone can no longer support life. This process of
overenrichment occurs in the ocean as algal growth. The algae
grows to the extent that sunlight is blocked from the rest of the
depths, and the dissolved oxygen that other organisms need to
live becomes depleted, killing off all or nearly all fish and crustacean life in the zone. The size of a dead zone varies but is usually around 20,000 square kilometers (about 7,700 square miles).
Nearly two-thirds of the surface area of estuaries and bays in the
United States is now overenriched, and large zones of eutrophication have also occurred in the North Sea, the Baltic Sea, the
Adriatic Sea, the Black Sea, and Japan's inland Seto Sea (Pew
Oceans Commission 2001). Although it is difficult to economically quantify such a loss of life, we do know that eutrophication
prevents both the economic and the subsistence extraction of living resources from the area. If the explosive growth in algae (an
algae bloom) contains an abundance of toxic plankton, human illness caused by poisoning may also occur.

Oil Pollution

Oil pollution deserves specific attention as an ocean problem.
Some estimates place the total amount of oil spilled, dumped, or
otherwise placed in the ocean by humans at 5.8 billion gallons (or
20 million tons) a year, half of which is from oil tankers. (Some oil
pollution comes from natural seepages on the ocean floor.) Most
estimates are lower, however, both in the amount of total oil pollution and the contribution by tankers.

Oil pollution is managed by the regime of the 1973/1978
International Convention for the Prevention of Pollution from
Ships (MARPOL), which is credited for a 60 percent decrease in
accidental oil spill pollution (see chapter 6 for oil spill data). Oil
pollution policy is generally reactive, not proactive. The prede-
cessor to MARPOL, the 1954 International Convention for the

Prevention of Pollution of the Sea by Oil (OILPOL), demonstrates this problem. This section will show how international oil regulation has evolved through the history of these two conventions.

In 1929, the world's largest tanker was just under 18 tons. By the 1950s, vessels of this type commonly surpassed 50,000 tons. And by 1970, 60 percent of the world's oil was being transported by tankers that were up to 100,000 tons or more. OILPOL was created to handle this growing oil transportation industry. Unfortunately, OILPOL must be judged inadequate as a regime because it did not define its scope (area of relevance) in detail. OILPOL would only manage a portion of intentional oil pollution, while taking no precautions against accidental oil pollution.

Intentional, or operational, oil pollution occurs on a regular basis when ships put ocean water in their oil cargo tanks after the oil has been unloaded at port. The water is used to provide stability for the large, empty tankers. The vessels then release this contaminated water back into the ocean when it is no longer needed. However, the tanks still have oil residue in them, and this residue mixes with the water to create a sludgelike pollutant. In response to the regular dumping of this material, OILPOL established a 50-mile belt around national coastlines where pollution was prohibited. Unfortunately, pollution was narrowly defined in this context as a certain amount of "persistent" oils— only "crude, lubricating oil, diesel, and other heavy oils, were to be counted as pollutants. They believed that light oils such as gasoline . . . were non-polluting" (Barkdull 1993, 118). Meanwhile, accidental oil pollution would not be taken seriously until a major tragedy occurred.

In 1967, the *Torrey Canyon,* a Liberian tanker carrying nearly 120,000 tons of crude oil, grounded off the coast of England. It spilled half its load on the coast and contaminated hundreds of miles of shoreline in England and along the French Brittany coast. OILPOL did not have a protocol for accidents, and as a result, there were no special international agreements about how to begin cleanup efforts. Consequently, England and France could not start dealing with the tanker itself until the captain legally abandoned the ship. The attempts to handle the oil began with the application of detergents that were later discovered to be damaging in themselves. The ordeal eventually concluded with the tanker being bombed to the bottom of the ocean in hopes that the remaining oil would be burned off in the process. Instead, the tanker and its oil just sank to the bottom, and the entire cargo slipped out into the water.

The *Torrey Canyon* disaster revealed deep problems with OILPOL. The International Maritime Organization, the agency that administers international ship management schemes, met afterward. A new agreement in the form of MARPOL would come to replace OILPOL. MARPOL required that tankers have segregated ballast tanks, as well as devices to monitor and control discharges. As a result of the *Torrey Canyon* incident, MARPOL would also require that cargo tanks be divided into smaller holds so that if one hold ruptured, only the oil from that tank would spill. However, that was the extent of MARPOL's precautions for accidents, and it would not be until the *Exxon Valdez* spill that double hulls would become the subject of a serious policy discussion.

Also as a result of the *Torrey Canyon* spill, the liability cap for shipowners was raised, in the Protocol to Amend the International Convention on Civil Liability for Oil Pollution Damage (CLC). Liability caps are limits on how much a shipowner must pay for pollution cleanup in the event of a spill. In 1984, the liability cap was set at $62 million (Gallagher 1990, 605). This amount has increased over time, but the costs of cleanup and damage from an oil spill usually far exceed the maximum amount the shipowner is responsible for paying. Consequently, this regime has been called "very generous toward the shipowner." In fact, "in most instances, the owner would be responsible for damages up to the salvage of value of the ship. In the case of the *Torrey Canyon*, this meant the value of one lifeboat" (Barkdull 1993, 136).

The Case of the *Exxon Valdez*

On March 24, 1989, the *Exxon Valdez* made history by running aground on the coast of Alaska in Prince William Sound. The images of dying birds covered in oil became symbols of a neglectful multinational oil corporation and unprepared state and national governments. The *Exxon Valdez* accident would create unspeakable damage, but the real lesson from the spill was that it could have been prevented with some simple and reasonable precautions. Unfortunately, the Alaskan coastline still has not fully recovered.

Late on the night of March 23, the *Exxon Valdez* tanker left its Alaskan harbor. The captain supervised the vessel out of the immediate area only to find icebergs in the shipping lane (a designated route for ships). He then ordered his exhausted crew to exit the lane to avoid the icebergs and turn back into the lane afterward the danger was passed. After he gave these instructions, he retired to his cabin. But the crew never returned the ship back into the shipping lane. As a result, the tanker ran aground on a reef that cut open the hull, releasing 200,000 gallons of oil per minute from the single-hulled supertanker.

Just under 11 million gallons of oil spilled into the ocean, covering 2,592 miles of coastline (see Figure 2.1). The largest oil spill in U.S. history, it killed 250,000 seabirds, 250 bald eagles, 2,800 to 3,500 sea otters, 22 orca (killer whales), and millions of fish, and it destroyed billions of salmon and herring eggs (*Exxon Valdez* Oil Spill Trustee Council 2001; Jenkins and Kastner 2000; "The Exxon Valdez" 1999). In addition, four people lost their lives as a result of activities related to the cleanup (Alaska Oil Spill Commission 1990). Monetary damages for the spill have been estimated to be as much as $900 *billion* (Gallagher 1990, 572 n. 4).

The oil spill may have been one of the worst environmental disasters in U.S. history, similar in importance to the Three Mile Island and the Love Canal disasters. Nonetheless, Exxon has stated that it has done enough after spending $2.5 billion in cleanup costs and $1 billion in studies and conservation in Prince William Sound. "We have spent $3.5 billion. *We think we acted as a good corporate citizen,*" said Exxon spokesperson Tom Cirigliano in response to a $5.3 billion award of damages to Alaskan plaintiffs. "We don't think punitive damages are warranted" (Dinesh 2000, emphasis added). The U.S. Supreme Court has declined to hear complaints that the case was tainted with improprieties, and in November 2001, the Ninth Circuit Court of Appeals ruled that the $5 billion award was about 66 percent excessive and ordered a lower court to reestablish the amount. Environmental and fishing groups have said the ruling is unfair and that "Exxon is getting let off the hook. . . . They have committed environmental atrocities, and they are not being made to pay the price for it" (Nieves 2001).

In several accounts, the blame for the spill has been laid at the feet of the tanker captain, Joseph Hazelwood. Captain Hazelwood was found to be intoxicated at the scene by the Coast Guard. Eleven hours after the grounding, his blood alcohol content was .061. (Federal law does not allow crew members to operate a vessel with a blood alcohol content of .04 or more.) Hazelwood was immediately fired by the corporation. Later, he would be acquitted of felony charges that were the marine equivalent of driving under the influence, but he would have to pay $50,000 in fines and perform a thousand hours of community

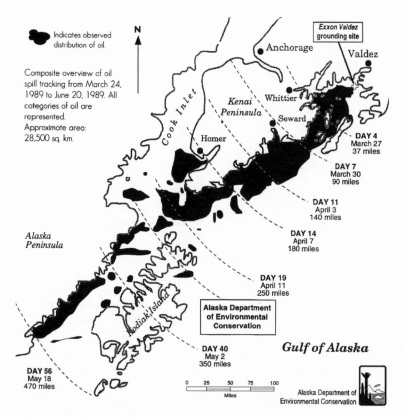

Figure 2.1 *Exxon Valdez* Oil Spill

Source: Map courtesy of the *Exxon Valdez* Oil Spill Trustee Council.

service for misdemeanor oil discharge (Alaska Oil Spill Commission 1990).

Some environmentalists have argued that Exxon made Captain Hazelwood a scapegoat for the *Exxon Valdez* problem in order to defend itself both in court and in public opinion. If the corporation could show that the spill was an individual's fault, the weight of public condemnation would shift from Exxon to Hazelwood. However, there are indications that Exxon knew of the captain's drinking problem prior to the accident and that, beyond the personal habits of any one man, the real problems were at the corporate and policy levels. The final report of the Alaska Oil Spill Commission placed the ultimate responsibility on a combination of "neglectful" factors:

> The response capabilities of Alyeska Pipeline Service Company to deal with the spreading sea of oil would be tested and found to be both unexpectedly slow and woefully inadequate. The worldwide capabilities of Exxon Corp. would mobilize huge quantities of equipment and personnel to respond to the spill—but not in the crucial first few hours *and days* when containment and cleanup efforts are at a premium. The U.S. Coast Guard would demonstrate its prowess at ship salvage, protecting crews and lightering operations, but prove utterly incapable of oil spill containment and response (Alaska Oil Spill Commission 1990, emphasis added).

In other words, the spill would not have been as catastrophic as it was had the corporation and the government been prepared for such an eventuality. As it was, under the prevailing flat, calm ocean conditions, the oil took three days to spread across the coastline.

Most of this oil could have been skimmed off the top of the water before it covered the beach. Exxon and the Coast Guard failed to react quickly because there was confusion over who was responsible for responding to the scene. Also, although the company that maintains the Alaskan Pipeline, Alyeska Pipeline Service Company, had a barge to respond to oil spills, the barge was out of commission at the time; moreover, it did not have the capacity to contain and gather a large quantity of oil.

Policy changed as a result of the spill. It was painfully obvious that double hulls on tankers could make a real difference. Double hulls protect the oil from spilling out if the first hull layer is torn open by a reef, iceberg, rock, or other hazard. Any large oil tanker built after 1996 is required to have a double hull, and existing single-hulled tankers will be phased out of operation in all international waters by 2015 (International Maritime Organization 2001).

In the United States, the Oil Pollution Act of 1990 was passed as a direct result of the *Exxon Valdez* spill. This act forces oil companies to be prepared for a major oil spill, and it bars single-hulled tankers from U.S. waters beginning in 2010.

Even policy for Prince William Sound changed as a result of the spill. Barges and booms to collect oil are now available at all times. Moreover, when a tanker goes through the sound, it is accompanied by two escort vessels and a trained tanker pilot who steers the ship, and it is followed by a satellite system that tracks the progress of ships in the area. Meanwhile, the *Exxon Valdez* has been banned from Prince William Sound, but the ship still operates in the Atlantic under a new name—*Sea River Mediterranean.* All of these changes could have been made prior to the spill, but policymakers were not forced to be proactive because little attention was focused on such concerns before that event. Now that these precautions are in place in one area of Alaska, however, one question persists: why are some of these precautions not being taken in many more areas with regularity? Perhaps the answer has much to do with the power and politics of "Big Oil."

The overall lesson of the *Exxon Valdez* incident is that environmental regulatory policy is reaction oriented. As a consequence, environmental policy must often wait until a well-attended cataclysm occurs before policymakers are finally convinced to take action. In some cases, as in the *Exxon Valdez* spill, this action may come too late.

The United Nations Regional Seas Programme

In 1974, the United Nations Environment Programme, concerned with managing pollution in regional areas, designed the Regional Seas Programme. This programme divides the World Ocean into sixteen regional sections (see chapter 6). Each region then develops its own ocean management in a way that reflects its individualized needs and opportunities in handling pollution and coastal waters.

The Regional Seas Programme is best understood as an outline for developing ocean policy, and it provides step-by-step instructions for doing so. The first step is to identify problem areas. Regional planners then come up with a program to address these problems. Finally, the regional authorities design a regulatory structure to administer and implement the program. Since each area is individualized, the Regional Seas Programme allows for flexibility in tackling problems specific to locales.

This flexibility has resulted in notable diplomatic success. It has brought together historically antagonistic nations such as Israel and Libya, the United States and Cuba, and Iraq and Iran. The Regional Seas Programme has also garnered the support of many participants. A total of 140 nations, 40 international nongovernmental organizations, and 14 UN agencies are involved in this regime. Because of this diplomatic success, nations are now sharing information with each other and working together to improve their regional seas (UNEP 1999).

Flexibility, however, does have its drawbacks. One drawback is that the regions develop different rules, creating a patchwork of demands for ships that must work in multiple regions. This brings us to the "flags of convenience" issue mentioned earlier in the chapter. Most regulations on ships are administered by the flag state. A flag state is the country that grants the necessary flag to a vessel and is supposed to take responsibility for regulating that ship under the consequence of having the flag and permission to sail revoked. International shipping regimes typically rely on the flag state to enforce international laws and rules. To escape the costs of fulfilling the most demanding requirements of a strict country, ships may opt to fly the flags of more lenient nations. In other words, shipowners sometimes fly the flags of nations that demand less of them and their crews, even if the ships and crews are from a totally different region. The owners do this to escape regulation, taxation, labor laws, pollution limits, fishing regulations, and other controls that interfere with their profits.

The Regional Seas Programme provides individualized opportunities for local authorities to cope with problems that are not addressed in global regimes such as the Law of the Sea. In this way, regional areas do not have to wait for the rest of the world to agree with their plans. However, ships that cross multiple regions end up being subject to many different and possibly complex expectations. Despite this problem, the programme is generally considered a respectable success in terms of getting some states to address conservation needs that they otherwise might have ignored.

Mining and the "Common Heritage of Mankind"

For some nations, deep-sea mining is one of the most controversial issues related to the ocean. In fact, the United States and other industrial powers refused to ratify the United Nations Convention on the Law of the Sea because of disagreements over this very issue.

The most important concept to understand about deep-sea mining is the "common heritage of mankind." The Law of the Sea reads:

> Activities in the Area shall, as specifically provided for in this Part, be carried out for the benefit of mankind as a whole, irrespective of the geographical location of States, whether coastal or land-locked, and taking into particular consideration the interests and needs of developing States and of peoples who have not attained full independence or other self-governing status recognized by the United Nations . . . (XV) and other relevant General Assembly resolutions (United Nations 2001).

The common heritage of mankind is an idea that was introduced by the Maltese delegate to the United Nations, Arvid Pardoe. The concept specifically prescribes that all minerals taken from the deep seabed within "the Area" belong to and should benefit all of humankind, not just the countries that have the ability to retrieve said minerals. "The Area" is that section of the seabed under the high seas. Some scholars argue that most areas of the ocean, not just that particular part, should be the common heritage of all people.

Among the resources of the deep seabed are the manganese and polymetalic nodules that were discovered in the 1870s by the crew of the HMS *Challenger*. The nodules sit at the bottom of the ocean and resemble small, misshapen iron cannonballs. At the time of the *Challenger,* however, the technology did not exist to mine these minerals. As a result, it was not until 1958 that the Institute for Marine Resources at the University of California drew attention to the possibilities of practical deep-sea mining by reporting that oceanic mining could provide many minerals at 50 to 75 percent of the cost of mining on land (Juda 1996).

Since the minerals had been technically out of the reach of all countries, no nation had developed an economy dependent on deep-sea mining. Pardo saw this as an opportunity to make the minerals the communal property of the world and argued for the common heritage idea as a way to redistribute global wealth. He insisted that international seabeds and subsoils should be reserved as the common heritage; otherwise, the "strong would get stronger, the rich richer, and among the rich themselves there would arise an increasing and insuperable differentiation between two or three and the remainder" (Juda 1996, 189). Because weaker marine states did not have the same capacity to collect these minerals as strong marine powers, Pardoe wanted to make sure that the resources were not used to reproduce global inequity between rich and poor states.

One political result of Pardoe's idea was that industrialized countries balked at the Law of the Sea. In 1994, in an effort to overcome the resistance of the dissenting countries, a further agreement was made specific to Part XI, the section in the Law of the Sea that describes deep-sea mining. The premise of this additional agreement was that private industry should be allowed to mine the area alongside the International Seabed Authority (ISA), the agency that administers deep-sea mining there. According to the original intent of the common heritage idea, the mining of the area would be solely an international public works effort. Some analysts say this extra agreement actually bargained away the major benefits for the world's poor, since private industry would essentially be competing against the international governing efforts. Industrial nations, however, were not willing to totally replace profit with charity (Borgese 1998), and they can now lease rights to mine in the area. Eventually, industrialized countries won their preference by threatening to abandon the whole Law of the Sea Treaty, and the extra agreement was adopted. The United States has continued to dissent despite this extra agreement, but "developed and developing states alike have now widely accepted the Convention as modified by the 1994 Agreement" (Noyes 1998, 117). The ISA began leasing operations in 1996 from its headquarters in Kingston, Jamaica, though actual commercial mining has not yet occurred due to high costs associated with this endeavor.

In summary, the deep-seabed mining debate has been about the global redistribution of wealth as much as it has been about geology and marine science. Redistribution of global wealth usually implies a transfer of wealth from industrialized, developed nations to disadvantaged, developing nations. Consequently, the tension surrounding deep-seabed mining has stemmed, in large part, from a more generalized tension about redistributing wealth.

Jurisdictions and Disputes

Jurisdictions carve up the world's oceans into many different areas of control. For this reason, some analysts have said that the Law of the Sea defies the organic and connected nature of the oceans themselves: the oceans do not know or necessarily change where exclusive economic zones begin or end. However, ocean management is more viable when there is a way to control the use of and access to marine resources. Controlling the oceans' benefits in that regard is the function of current ocean jurisdictions. This section will examine these jurisdictions and their important components that apply to ocean management. First, the internal seas, the territorial seas, and the exclusive economic zones will be described. Next, the archipelago baselines—the specific rights of landlocked and "geographically disadvantaged" states—will be examined. Finally, the Law of the Sea dispute settlement regime will be discussed.

The Primary Jurisdictions: Internal Seas, Territorial Seas, and Exclusive Economic Zones

The most important jurisdictions are the 12-mile territorial seas, the 200-mile exclusive economic zones, the continental shelf exception, and the open seas. These areas are vital in terms of the amount of resources they contain and the geophysical protection they offer as security buffers vis-à-vis other states.

The first jurisdiction area is that of the internal seas. Internal seas are semienclosed by geographic characteristics of the land and sea, such as inlets, bays, and other similar places where land forms a full or partial barrier to the rest of the ocean. Internal seas are legally the same as territorial seas in that they are under the full sovereignty of the nation to which they belong. Should a border between nations fall in internal seas, the nations involved must negotiate how those waters will be divided.

A coastal state may claim waters extended 12 miles out from its coastline as its territorial sea. The coastal state has complete sovereignty over the entire water column in the territorial sea. The water column comprises the airspace above the ocean, the benthic zone (the seafloor and below), and the pelagic zone (all of the ocean in between). The state has the right to exploit and develop that area as it desires, with occasional deference to previous agreements (such as an agreement to halt whaling).

Within the territorial seas, states usually permit the "safe passage" or "innocent passage" of foreign ships, though this is not usually allowed in internal seas. Safe passage is the preference given to passing ships that have a peaceful intent. Part II of the Law of the Sea defines passage as "innocent so long as it is not prejudicial to the peace, good order or security of the coastal State" (United Nations 2001). Thus, ships using safe passage are trusted to navigate through the area without causing violence or disruptions to the coastal state. Coastal states are allowed to place temporary holds on safe passage through their territorial seas for reasons of national security, but the safe passage provision is intended to keep shipping lanes open as a norm. Also, the safe passage of ships requires that vessels heed the shipping laws of the coastal nation, and submarines must pass through on the surface, with their flags raised.

An exclusive economic zone extends a maximum of 188 miles beyond the 12-mile territorial sea, allowing for a full 200-mile area of coastal state control. In this area, the coastal state controls scientific research, conservation measures, fishing regulation, mining, and shipping lanes, but legally, it only maintains "sovereign rights" over the area as opposed to "sovereignty." The difference is small, but in general, a jurisdiction of sovereign rights confers less control than a jurisdiction of sovereignty. In an EEZ, other states have the right to use the zone for overflight, navigation, and laying undersea cables, according to certain limits. The law for navigation through an EEZ is also different and more lenient than in the territorial sea. In an EEZ, foreign ships may make "transit passage"; further, "unlike innocent passage, transit passage may not be suspended by the coastal state [and it] applies to aircraft as well as to ships, and . . . to submerged vessels, which do not have to surface and show their flag" (Juda 1996, 227).

Archipelagic Baselines

Island jurisdictions have been especially controversial because small island states that previously had little jurisdiction in the open ocean have now come to control large ocean blocks. The controversy has recently been settled under UNCLOS-III.

Archipelagic states, or states that are composed of an island or multiple islands, have experienced a windfall by establishing exclusive economic zones. The fact that island states wanted to set up EEZs did not, in itself, stir up any controversy, but just how those zones would be marked off did spark heated debate. At issue was where the baselines for the EEZ should be drawn. If the lines *connected* the islands belonging to one state, rather than simply running around each island, some countries stood to gain hundreds of miles of ocean waters lying between the landmasses that made up their country. As it turns out, island states did prevail in this regard—but not without a struggle.

During UNCLOS, one group that emerged to fight for connecting baselines was made up of the Pacific island countries (PICs). PICs were supported by the large Third World bloc, which had significant bargaining power at UNCLOS-III due to its increasing majority. PICs had earlier demanded that the areas between islands become internal waters, but this idea had been dismissed at the first two UNCLOS conventions. During UNCLOS-III, however, this demand was given a legitimate forum. In the end, the marine powers' fight to keep archipelagic waters open failed, and the baselines drawn around island nations created territorial seas. Thus, these states gained power over the transit in their adjacent and interconnecting waters. As Part IV, Article 52, of UNCLOS reads: "The archipelagic State may, without discrimination in form or in fact among foreign ships, suspend temporarily in specified areas of its archipelagic waters the innocent passage of foreign ships if such suspension is essential for the protection of its security" (United Nations 2001). Thus, the area of national control increased dramatically in the Pacific by assigning baselines that connected island states and most of the water between them.

As a result, the archipelagic resource base also increased dramatically. For example, PICs now control the world's largest tuna stocks. Surprisingly, though, the nations have only received marginal benefit from these new resources. Most of the fishing that occurs in the PIC areas is done by non-PIC industry. Also, PICs have not been able to command significant fees for their fisheries because they have not been able to bargain as a group. Since the fish stocks travel within this region, if one island nation sells its fish for a low price it undermines other PICs that are demanding a higher price for the same fish

(Schurman 1998). For the Pacific island countries, therefore, the archipelagic baselines were an initial victory, but PICs have yet to turn that win into real control of the market forces within their new jurisdictions.

Rights of Landlocked and Geographically Disadvantaged States

Most countries in the world have adequate access to the ocean. Those that do not are at a significant economic disadvantage. As a result, the struggle of landlocked and geographically disadvantaged states (LL/GDS) became an issue at UNCLOS-III.

LL/GDS states are countries that do not have good access to the ocean. In general, states without coastlines are more likely to be poor and have lower economic growth rates than nations with good access to the ocean (Hausmann 2001). LL/GDS have therefore fought to gain preferential access to other nations' resources in nearby EEZs.

UNCLOS gives LL/GDS equal access rights to a regional EEZ. However, those rights lack substantive terms. Beyond noting that such states need to be considered when a nearby coastal state decides what to do with a surplus in its EEZ, the degree of preference granted to the LL/GDS is not well defined.

The right to merely be considered has not provided significant benefits for LL/GDS nations. That weak jurisdictional claims evolved may be partially explained by the fact that the LL/GDS lobby at UNCLOS, which did not have many members, was itself weak. In the end, the apparent lack of interest in the LL/GDS may reflect the simple reality that the ocean is readily available to most people in the world.

Law of the Sea Dispute Resolution

As the preceding section has demonstrated, jurisdiction agreements are controversial and do not end all disputes surrounding their use. To handle the anticipated load of disputes that will arise in the future, the Law of the Sea has established a judicial institution to hear the issues and make binding decisions. Dispute settlement under UNCLOS can take several forms. It can be forged in informal mechanisms, an ad hoc third-party tribunal, the International Court of Justice (ICJ), or the International Tribunal for the Law of the Sea (ITLS).

Unlike the International Court of Justice, the ITLS can hear the cases of nongovernmental organizations, as well as corporations under specific limitations (they need to be designated by a state party to the Law of the Sea as a legitimate agent). The International Seabed Authority is involved in determining certain controversial measures for mining, and it may also be a party in this court. Under UNCLOS, any state and some specific nonstate parties may request a legally binding decision from the ITLS. Although the provision for the obligatory third-party adjudication of disputes was controversial, John Noyes (1998, 117) noted that "the Convention's dispute settlement provisions posed no obstacle to states' acceptance of the Convention and indeed, have garnered favorable comments by national officials."

The settlement procedure was not without its compromises and deals, however. For example, disputes over so-called surplus living resources (such as fish) in an EEZ, the measure of an allowable catch, or the capacity for harvest do not obligate a coastal state to the decision of a third party. Grievances from parties interested in the decision involving coastal states in such matters may demand "conciliation," but the outcome of this conciliation is not binding or guaranteed. Parties may also request a member of any nationality of their choosing to be on the bench, and each geographic group that is represented in the United Nations must have at least three members available. Twenty-one judges sit on a case at a time.

Suggestions for the Future

The conclusion of this chapter will offer suggestions for future efforts to devise ocean policy. Some of the key problems that have been identified will be addressed, including, among others, fisheries, whaling, and pollution. Common to all of these problems is the fact that the precautionary principle—deciding to err on the side of caution regarding ecological use and exploitation—is a less expensive, less difficult, and more effective mechanism than other policy interventions that are needed after ecological damage has occurred. Unfortunately, it is often politically infeasible to use precaution until the danger of overexploitation has become obvious, apparent, and imminent. A key to sustainable ocean conservation in the future will be the acceptance of this fact. Until policy communities adopt this principle as the foundation for ocean policies, policymaking will likely be reactionary and fragmented. For example, policy is now focused on dealing with single fishery collapses rather than on making global connections to global ecosystem threats and their related causes.

Fishing

Overfishing is not inevitable. Ocean managers can use certain proven remedies to curb the problem. However, to accomplish this, the causes of overfishing, including the issues of open access and overcapitalization, must be handled effectively. The use of fisher quotas and marine protected areas can help in this effort.

Individual fisher quotas (IFQs) assign individual fishers a limit of fish (a quota) in a particular fishery, while keeping other fishers from entering the resource pool. Since fishers do not have to worry about a tragedy of the commons, they are not racing against their competitors to land fewer and fewer fish. Instead, they are working to get a known and stable amount of fish. And in the process, they can afford to take their time and focus attention on cultivating the fishery for health and sustainability. Thus, IFQs may "reverse the race to overcapitalize, because they encourage fishermen to downsize and adopt fishing practices more suitable to producing higher valued products year-round" (Hsu and Wilen 1997, 807).

Fishing cooperatives such as IFQs have been shown to successfully reduce by-catch by over 50 percent. They also have been shown to nearly double the amount of yield (the amount of edible, unprocessed fish caught) as quickly as one year after implementation. The main point, however, is that open access does not work well in light of modern commercial fishing. If fisheries are to become sustainable, fishing conservation must limit access to them in some manner.

Another important policy tool is the use of marine protected areas (MPAs). Protective areas can take the form of sanctuaries for certain species (for instance, whale sanctuaries), no-pollution zones (such as the Great Barrier Reef), and no-fishing zones. Evidence suggests that marine protected areas and no-fishing zones in general, even if they are only of marginal size, can bring an area back to life.

> There is growing evidence that closing areas to fishing can benefit fisheries while meeting a broad range of other marine management objectives [including] increased abundance and size of individuals [fish]

within NFZs [no-fishing zones]; emigration of target species from reserves to adjacent fishing grounds— "the spillover effect"; increased production of eggs and larvae and export of these to adjacent fisheries, and increased fertilization success due to density effects; and protection of habitat for spawning and settlement of eggs and larvae (Wells and Hildesley 1999, 83).

In other words, MPAs allow fisheries to recover. And when fish recover, the ecological, economic, and cultural systems that depend on fishing also become stronger.

Thus, IFQs or fishing cooperatives and the designation of marine protected areas provide some solutions to the problem of overfishing. One obstacle to this set of policies is the anticipated political opposition that fishers may raise in order to protect their short-term interests. To help fishers—especially smaller, independent fishers—survive short-term cutbacks in fish, governments may consider short-term subsidies to keep them in business. This may assuage the fishers' fears about going out of business while they await the long-term benefits that will come with a stronger industry and ecosystem. In addition, since so many people depend on fish and fishing to live, one effect of stronger and healthier fisheries is an increase in regional and global security (Westing 1992).

Whaling

Whaling management—where it is being adhered to—appears to be working because whale populations have been rising gradually over the years (see chapter 6). However, whales reproduce slowly, and this immediate success should not be considered permanent even though the IWC has had a remarkable effect on curbing the commercial harvest of whales.

That being said, the IWC would become irrelevant if whaling nations decided to ignore its provisions and begin whaling again. If commercial whaling resumes, the revised management plan offers a compromise that features a conservative approach to estimating wildlife populations. Unfortunately, the revised plan has been unable to resolve the question of whether whaling nations will be able to keep their fleets from taking too many animals or the wrong whale species, from wasting their catches, and from using the inhumane hunting techniques that have notoriously plagued the industry. If whaling nations successfully force the issue of reinstituting whaling, these ethical and practical considerations should weigh heavily in the negotiations.

Sea-Level Rise

Sea-level rise, in combination with global warming, may be one of the most severe environmental threats of the modern epoch. Although scientists will not be able to say with absolute certainty that global warming is occurring and that human activity is behind both global warming and sea-level rises, the evidence is mounting. Under the "precautionary principle" that demands policymakers err on the side of caution in the face of uncertainty, the first step in dealing with these two related problems is to assume global warming is occurring. Waiting for certainty may well mean waiting for human catastrophe. The worst offenders in terms of greenhouse gas pollution should be the first targets for reductions, just as delegates to the Kyoto Protocol agreed.

The United States stands out as one of the most consequential nations because it emits more greenhouse gases than any other country in the world but refuses to reign in its pollution. Even if the Kyoto Protocol were to treat less industrialized countries in the same way as industrialized countries as a matter of fairness (as leaders in Washington demand), it is doubtful that U.S. leaders and U.S. corporations would see it in their interest to reduce their emissions. This situation is a real tragedy of the commons because it is difficult to see how other political actors in the world can force the United States to stop cooking the planet. Yet it is crucial that the United States reduce its emissions and use the energy-efficient technologies that it has already developed, such as fuel-cell energy. At the same time, U.S. citizens who believe this to be an important cause can help by reducing their driving and energy consumption as much as possible until cleaner technologies make it into car dealerships and homes. They could also put pressure on the federal government to agree to the Kyoto Protocol.

In addition, the political divide between the North (industrialized countries) and the South (lesser industrialized countries) has added to a false dichotomy of development/pollution or no development/no pollution. Development as a concept should mean more than industrialization. Redefining global notions of development to include human well-being and sustainability, as

Agenda 21 has attempted to do (see chapter 7), is one way of getting around the North-South problem. However, to redefine development in this way, poverty must be eliminated and nations with concentrations of wealth cannot produce more than their share of atmospheric pollution.

One way to implement this may be to institute a greenhouse gas emissions tax. This tax could be geared toward luxury emissions instead of survival emissions, that is, emissions produced by most cars, excessive household energy consumption, and recreation vehicles such as all-terrain vehicles and boats. The tax would be justified by the fact that greenhouse gas emitters do not pay the full cost of global warming (consider the costs associated with the 100 million coastal residents who may lose their homes in the next 100 years). The revenues from this tax could be applied toward sustainable improvements for human lifestyles, such as public transit, energy-efficient technologies, architecture, and urban planning (including that focused on avoiding urban sprawl). These revenues could be treated as global revenues and directed to less industrialized countries, allowing them to improve the living conditions of their people—but not at the expense of the atmosphere or the sea level. This type of tax could not begin to pay for such planetary costs, but it may be a tool to redistribute the benefits of emissions while slowing their production.

Ocean Pollution

Oil pollution regimes have been reactionary and insufficiently preventive, as evidenced by the *Exxon Valdez* case and other massive oil spills. This situation may be caused by the undue influence of the petroleum industry, which has largely created its own regulations (Barkdull 1993). The MARPOL regime may benefit from increased NGO observation and reporting to inspire proactive policy work. Precautions that would help stop or contain procedural or accidental oil pollution should be implemented before the fact and aggressively. It may be helpful for the IMO to establish a strong research and development fund; innovative ways of generating new and better protective measures could be funded by taxing the oil industry with navigational fees for the use of and risk to the ocean. In that way, researchers would not have to wait to be funded by the petroleum industry itself. Of course, a decrease in the transport and use of petroleum as a result of a growing dependence on renewable energy sources is a desirable option as well. The most pressing obstacle that impedes this kind of management progress is the power of the large oil companies, which have successfully stalled preventive oil pollution policy since the 1950s as a means of protecting their profits. One way to overcome this huge obstacle is to take advantage of citizen groups and nongovernmental organizations that can provide some balance to the political pressure applied by the oil companies. If pollution policies are to be proactive, policymakers will have to be willing to face this struggle head-on.

Jurisdictions

The Law of the Sea provides a number of good ways to solve disputes. However, the United States cannot in good faith participate in ocean jurisdictions and dispute resolution without ratifying the treaty. Many analysts and groups have called on Washington to relinquish its allegiance to the freedom of the seas doctrine in favor of a more just common heritage ethic. The United States should ratify UNCLOS: it is the legal regime that most of the world observes, particularly when it comes to jurisdictions, and the United States adheres to a great deal of the treaty anyway. Although UNCLOS is weak in certain areas, such as environmental protection, even federal administrative agencies that work with the ocean recognize that it is now common international law.

UNCLOS admittedly has many flaws, but few political agreements acknowledge the interrelatedness of the oceans. In addition, UNCLOS enjoys broad support that was negotiated by "the most widely attended gathering of governmental representatives in history" (Pinto 1992, 53). Compared to the mare liberum doctrine, which was created by naval monopolies and the desire for infinite harvests, the Law of the Sea is an institution that protects the ocean's common heritage from unmitigated self-interest. By creating well-established rules, expectations, and jurisdictions for the World Ocean, the Law of the Sea prevents the same tragedy of the commons that the free seas ethic inspires. Consequently, the Law of the Sea builds an environmental security that brings global well-being closer to home. It makes sense for the United States to forsake its isolationism and join the rest of the world in this effort. If this is to occur, the U.S. Senate will have to move the treaty to a vote, which probably will happen only with the application of significant political pressure.

References

Alaska Oil Spill Commission. 1990. *SPILL: The Wreck of the Exxon Valdez, Final Report*. Available online at http://www.oilspill.state.ak.us/facts/details.html. Accessed on November 11, 2002.

Andresen, Steinar. 1998. "The Making and Implementation of Whaling Policies: Does Participation Make a Difference?" In David Victor, Kal Raustiala, and Eugene Skolnikoff, eds., *The Implementation and Effectiveness of International Environmental Commitments: Theory and Practice*. Cambridge, MA: MIT Press.

"Antarctic Key to Sudden Sea Level Rise in the Past." 2002. *Science Daily*. April 1. Available online at http://sciencedaily.com. Accessed on November 11, 2002.

Barkdull, John. 1993. "The Formation of the Marine Oil Pollution Regime: A Case of Institutional Bargaining." Ph.D. diss. University of Wisconsin, Madison.

Birnie, Patricia. 1996. "Regimes Dealing with the Oceans and All Kinds of Seas from the Perspective of the North." In Oran Young, George Demko, and Kilaparti Ramakrishna, eds., *Global Environmental Change and International Governance*. Hanover, NH: University Press of New England.

Borgese, Elisabeth Mann. 1998. *The Oceanic Circle: Governing the Seas as a Global Resource*. New York: United Nations University Press.

Cicin-Sain, Biliana, and Robert Knecht. 1998. *Integrated Coastal and Ocean Management: Concepts and Practices*. Washington, DC: Island Press.

Corbett, James, and Paul Fischbeck. 1997. "Emissions from Ships: Pollution and Policy Implications." *Science* 278, no. 5339: 832–834.

Dinesh, Manimoli. "Supreme Court Denies Appeal of $5 Billion in *Exxon Valdez* Damages." 2000. *Oil Daily* 50, no. 190 (October 3).

Douglas, Bruce, Michael Kearney, and Stephen Leatherman. 2001. *Sea Level Rise: History and Consequence*. New York: Academic Press, p. 3.

Dubner, Barry Hart. 1997. "Human Rights and Environmental Disaster: Two Problems That Defy the 'Norms' of the International Law of Sea Piracy." *Syracuse Journal of International Law and Commerce* 23, no. 1: 1–65.

Egan, Timothy. 2002. "On Hot Trail of Tiny Killer in Alaska." *New York Times*, June 25.

Exxon Valdez Oil Spill Trustee Council. 2001. "Questions and Answers." Available online at http://www.oilspill.state.ak.us/facts/qanda.html. Accessed on November 11, 2002.

"The *Exxon Valdez:* Stains That Remain." *Economist* 350 (March 20, 1999): 35.

Fairlie, Simon. 1998. "Fisheries: Confrontation and Violence in the Management of Marine Resources." In Mohamed Suliman, ed., *Ecology, Politics, and Violent Conflict*. New York: Zed Books.

Faith, Jeremy. 1996. "Enforcement of Fishing Regulations in International Waters: Piracy or Protection—Is Gunboat Diplomacy the Only Means Left?" *Loyola of Los Angeles International and Comparative Law Journal* 19: 199–221.

Frankel, Ernst. 1995. *Ocean Environmental Management: A Primer on the Role of the Oceans and How to Maintain Their Contributions to Life on Earth.* Englewood Cliffs, NJ: Prentice-Hall.

Gallagher, John. 1990. "In the Wake of the *Exxon Valdez*: Murky Legal Waters of Liability and Compensation." *New England Law Review* 25 (Winter): 571–616.

GESAMP (IMO/FAO/UNESCO–IOC/WMO/WHO/IAEA/UN/UNEP Joint Group of Experts on the Scientific Aspects of Marine Environmental Protection) and Advisory Committee on Protection of the Sea. 2001. *A Sea of Troubles*. GESAMP no. 70, 35 pp. ISBN 82-7701-010-9.

Gill, Martin. 1996. "Security at Sea: Fraud, Piracy and the Failure of Police Cooperation Internationally." *International Relations* 13, no. 3: 43–58.

Givens, Geof. 1999. "Multicriterion Decision Merging: Competitive Development of an Aboriginal Whaling Management Procedure." *Journal of American Statistical Association* 94, no. 448: 1003–1015.

Goodman, Timothy. 1999. "'Leaving the Corsair's Name to Other Times': How to Enforce the Law of Sea Piracy in the 21st Century through Regional International Agreements." *Case Western Reserve Journal of International Law* 31, no. 107: 139–168.

Hausmann, Ricardo. 2001. "Prisoners of Geography." *Foreign Policy* (January-February): 44–53.

Hsu, Shi-Ling, and James E. Wilen. 1997. "Ecosystem Management and the 1996 Sustainable Fisheries Act." *Ecology Law Quarterly* 24: 799–811.

Hyvarinen, Joy, Elizabeth Wall, and Inrani Lutchman. 1998. "The United Nations and Fisheries in 1998." *Ocean Development and International Law* 29: 323–338.

International Maritime Organization. 2001. Homepage. Available online at http://www.imo.org/home.asp. Accessed on August 11, 2002.

International Whaling Commission (IWC). 2001. Homepage. Available online at http://www.iwcoffice.org/. Accessed on November 11, 2002.

Jenkins, Robert, and Jill Kastner. 2000. "Running Aground in a Sea of Complex Litigation: A Case Comment on the *Exxon Valdez* Litigation." *UCLA Journal of Environmental Law and Policy* 18 (Summer): 1.

Juda, Lawrence. 1996. *International Law and Ocean Use Management: The Evolution of Ocean Governance.* New York: Routledge.

Krabil, W., W. Abdalati, E. Frederick, S. Manizade, C. Martin, J. Sonntag, R. Swift, R. Thomas, W. Wright, and J. Yungel. 2000. "Greenland Ice Sheet." *Science* 289, no. 5478 (July 21): 428–431.

National Research Council. 1997. *Striking a Balance: Improving Stewardship of Marine Areas.* Washington, DC: National Academy Press.

Nieves, Evelyn. 2001. "Court Overturns Jury Award in '89 *Exxon Valdez* Spill." *New York Times,* November 8, p. A14.

Noyes, John. 1998. "The International Tribunal for the Law of the Sea." *Cornell International Law Journal* 32: 109–182.

Pew Oceans Commission. 2001. *Marine Pollution in the United States.* Arlington, VA: Pew Oceans Commission.

Pinto, Christopher. 1992. "Maritime Security and the 1982 United Nations Convention on the Law of the Sea." In Josef Goldblatt, ed., *Maritime Security: The Building of Confidence.* New York: United Nations Press.

Prideaux, Margi. 2000. "The Complex Game of Protecting Whales." *Habitat Australia* 8 (August): 8.

Schurman, Rachel. 1998. "Tuna Dreams: Resource Nationalism and the Pacific Islands' Tuna Industry." *Development and Change* 29, no. 1: 107–135.

"So Much for Saving the Whales." 2000. *Newsweek,* April 17, p. 58.

United Nations. 1995. *United Nations Conference on Straddling Fish Stocks and Highly Migratory Fish Stocks.* Available online at http://gopher://gopher.un.org/00/LOS/CONF164/164_37.TXT. Accessed on January 25, 2002.

———. 2001. *United Nations Convention on the Law of the Sea.* Available online at http://www.un.org/Depts/los/index.htm. Accessed on January 25, 2002.

United Nations Division for Sustainable Development. 1999. "Protection of the Oceans, All Kinds of Seas, Including Enclosed and Semi-enclosed Seas, and Coastal Areas and the Protection, Rational Use and Development of Their Living Resources" in *Agenda 21.* Available online at http://www.un.org/esa/sustdev/agenda21chapter17.htm. Accessed on August 11, 2002.

United Nations Environment Programme (UNEP). 1999. *Regional Seas Programme.* Available online at http://www.unep.org/unep/program/natres/water/regseas/regseas.htm. Accessed on August 11, 2002.

———. 2000. *Global Environment Outlook 2000.* London: Earthscan Publishers.

United Nations Food and Agricultural Organization (FAO). 2000. *State of World Fisheries and Aquaculture*. Rome: FAO.

Vallega, Adalberto. 2001. *Sustainable Ocean Governance: A Geographical Perspective*. London and New York: Routledge.

Wells, Sue, and Meg Gawler. 1999. "Involving People in Marine Protected Areas: Experiences in Central America and Africa." In Sue Stolten and Nigel Dudley, eds., *Partnerships for Protection: New Strategies for Planning and Management for Protected Areas*. London: Earthscan Publications.

Wells, Sue, and Will Hildesley. 1999. "Future Development in Marine Protected Areas." In Sue Stolton and Nigel Dudley, eds., *Partnerships for Protection: New Strategies for Planning and Management for Protected Areas*. London: Earthscan Publications.

Westing, Arthur. 1992. "Environmental Dimensions of Maritime Security." In Josef Goldblatt, ed., *Maritime Security: The Building of Confidence*. New York: United Nations Press.

Wilder, Robert. 1998. *Listening to the Sea: The Politics of Improving Environmental Protection*. Pittsburgh, PA: University of Pittsburgh Press.

Williams, Nigel. 1998. "Over-fishing Disrupts Entire Ecosystem." *Science* 279, no. 5352: 809.

3

Ocean Security Dilemmas: Protecting the Oceans and Human Systems

Security is the state of having protection and being safe. Determining what or whom to protect and why that protection is needed is the subject of security politics and policy. More specifically, protecting nations is national security, protecting international peace is international security, protecting human well-being in general is human security, and protecting ecological functions of the earth is ecological security. On the whole, then, ocean security politics is the struggle to determine what or whom to protect from other navies, from piracy, from resource competition, and even from life-threatening environmental degradation.

This chapter will address policies of traditional military security, both national and international. Topics to be explored include the importance of naval power, "sea-lanes of communication," spheres of influence, balances of power, deterrence, and the post–Cold War international environment. A brief picture of the U.S. Navy will also be provided.

The rest of the chapter will focus on nonmilitary maritime security. First, the issue of piracy as a violent threat to ocean security will be addressed. Then, ecological ocean security will be explained, with attention paid to both "resource wars" and ecological threats that have life-and-death repercussions. Finally, the Law of the Sea and the Fishery Stock Agreement will be analyzed as they apply to these concepts and functions.

Military Ocean Security
The Importance of Naval Power

> Hee that commaunds the sea, commaunds the trade,
> and hee that is Lord of the trade of the world is Lord
> of the wealth of the worlde.
> —Sir Walter Raleigh (Padfield 2000, 2)

The World Ocean is an international domain where states come into contact with each other. Consequently, uses of the ocean affect the relationships between nations in several ways. In this section, the mechanics of traditional maritime security and sea power will be explained. This traditional ocean politics is what analysts usually mean when they use the term *maritime security* or *ocean security*.

Since most of the ocean is open for the navigation of warships, the ocean, unlike land, can be a place where the facilities of violence employed by one country come into regular contact with those of another country even if the respective nations are geographically distant from each other. The sea also allows for powerful navies to position themselves for attack against foreign nations without getting permission from neighbors to access the target's borders. For this and other reasons described here, the ocean is viewed by naval commanders as something like a chessboard. In this game, the players are well-armed military powers.

Nations that have been able to "project" themselves across the world with powerful navies have typically been among the more dominant countries throughout history for the very reason that they can impose violence from afar. In its function as a theater for military operations, the ocean was essential to the establishment and operation of European colonies. Colonial nations were, by definition, powerful naval nations as well.

Today, the World Ocean is still a physical medium through which powerful countries can enforce their foreign policy demands on nations with less powerful navies—this is what is meant by the term *gunboat diplomacy*. Usually, the term is employed outside the circumstance of war; hence, gunboat diplomacy is the threat of military force during peacetime, in order to achieve a goal. Many writers believe this kind of force explains a great deal of human history. Peter Padfield is one such writer.

Hailed as a seminal work, Padfield's *Maritime Supremacy and the Opening of the Western Mind* (2000, 1) declares boldly in the introduction:

> Maritime supremacy is the key which unlocks most, if not all, large questions of modern history, certainly the puzzle of how and why we—the Western democracies—are as we are. We are the heirs of maritime supremacy. Our civilization (if we can lay so large a claim), our beliefs, our dominance are products not of superior minds or bravery, cunning, greed or ruthlessness—common attributes of mankind—still less of the Christian religion, the "Protestant work ethic" or blind chance, but of the particular configuration of seas and land masses that has given the advantage to powers able to use and command the seas.

Although this is perhaps an overstatement, it is true that countries that have enjoyed military supremacy on the World Ocean have also enjoyed access to the world's markets, labor, and resources when others have not. As the discussion here should indicate, classical maritime security is fundamentally concerned with the dynamics and effects of maritime supremacy.

Sea-Lanes of Communication and Spheres of Influence

Traditional, or "realist," ocean security mechanics operate through the use of force by one nation on another nation. To do this on the ocean, control of ocean lanes and geographic regions is necessary. The concepts that function in this mode of thinking are sea-lanes of control and spheres of influence. These concepts will be considered in turn.

A sea-lane is an avenue enabling ships to pass on the ocean. Some avenues are more advantageous than others, especially for ship traffic that carries commodities from one country to another. Traffic for trade is still the primary use made of the ocean, and 90 percent of the world's goods are shipped by means of these sea-lanes. As a consequence, the ability to accumulate wealth is dependent on the control and accessibility of marine traffic.

Sea-lanes also are avenues for naval ships, and the access of naval ships to distant shores is important for the transport of weapons. Access to a sea-lane in the Mediterranean, for example, can provide military access for a distant power, such as the United States, to the Middle East. Use of sea-lanes by military and commercial ships is still "free" to this day under the remnants of mare liberum doctrine. However, when it comes to controlling navigation on the ocean, the primary factor may be sea power, not a doctrine. To the degree that a nation can affect passage of a commercial or naval vessel, it operates a "sea-lane of control." This ability becomes especially important during wartime when being able to control lanes of shipping means being able to move weapons, goods, and troops to critical locations. This control may also make it possible to deny the adversary the same advantages.

Some nations have historically had the benefit of controlling local seas (as Venice once did in the Mediterranean), whereas other nations have had a truly global reach—Spain, Portugal, the Netherlands, and the United States. If wealth is accumulated by trade, then these global powers can explain their wealth, in some measure, by the level of control they have exerted over important sea-lanes. During the fifteenth century, utter domination of the ocean lanes became possible with the advent of large guns and cannons that would decimate any rival unable to match this firepower.

Controlling specific sea-lanes meant having access to the most precious and wealth-related commodities. Today, this power is not very different, though trade has expanded from gold, sugar, and slaves to raw materials, oil, and manufactured goods. Controlling sea-lanes, then, is still a way to ensure the ability to access, move, and accumulate wealth and power.

The sea-lanes that are most important to control are those in areas where the ability for traffic to pass is limited and the space is small. The points at which sea-lanes become confined by land are called straits, but they can also be viewed as strategic "choke points." The Danish Straits, the Strait of Dover, the Strait of Gibraltar, the Bab el Mandeb, the Strait of Hormuz, the Malacca-Singapore Straits, the Sunda Straits, the Lombock Straits, Balabac Straits, Surigao Straits, Osumi-kaikyo, the Bering Strait, and the Strait of Magellan—almost all of which are concentrated in the Asian Pacific or Europe—are all choke points that have significant strategic importance (Vallega 2001).

Spheres of influence are geographic regions where a nation has a significant ability to decide what does or does not occur, especially in foreign policy. The term itself is a vague and imprecise one and is perhaps best illustrated with an example. The United States maintains a military base in Japan so that it can have a resource center and organizing headquarters for maritime operations in East Asia and the Middle East. Tokyo has shown that it is growing tired of its arrangement with the United States in this regard, but it had agreed to the base as a way for the United States to protect Japan from the Soviet Union, China, and the Koreas. Foreign bases such as the one in Japan increase the firepower that the United States has in place in the area, which demonstrates the U.S. "capability" to defend against other armed forces. *Capability* is the term used by security scholars to describe the ability of a nation to physically enforce and defend its threats, or signals, and to act on foreign aggression against itself or its allies. Because the United States has maintained a sphere of influence in East Asia, largely through Japan and its own aircraft carrier groups, it was able to act on a threatening signal against Taiwan, an ally.

Signals come in the form of official warnings and threats, movements of armed forces, and the use of physical warnings, such as shots fired across the bow of a ship. Signals allow for nations to demonstrate their intentions and capabilities. In 1995 and 1996, the People's Republic of China (PRC) became wary of independence movements within the Republic of China (Taiwan), and mainland China began testing missiles above Taiwan's airspace, actually shooting them over the island republic. China was signaling its capability and intent to enforce its "one China" policy, which holds that Taiwan is part of the mainland government. However, Taiwan had and continues to have (as of this writing) a defense arrangement with the United States that guarantees its safety from Chinese aggression, even though Washington acknowledges the one China policy. Consequently, after the PRC began its missile testing over Taiwan, the United States sent warships into the Taiwan Strait and signaled its own intent to uphold its arrangement with Taiwan. The ability to conduct this type of action relies on how much influence a nation has in distant regions. This kind of diplomacy is not unusual in world affairs, and had the United States not committed forces to protect Taiwan, other U.S. allies may have taken the lack of action as a signal that the United States was not a reliable ally.

War: Balances of Power, Arms Races, and Deterrence

The first way that the ocean affects war is as a protective buffer. Countries that have sea borders, as opposed to land borders, are more difficult to access for attack. The more sea borders a country has, the less likely it is to be attacked (Midlarsky 1995). Thus, the ocean has served as a first line of defense simply through its ability to keep enemies at bay.

Of course, powerful navies do not necessarily view a sea border as a buffer; instead, they may actually regard it as an access route. Navies that are well funded, armed, and equipped can find distant shores more accessible than the target country might like, and this may be a way in which a navy can be used to start a war.

Realist scholars point out that all of these moves on the global chessboard are ways to balance power, the dynamics of which they believe is the cause of war. As will be discussed, war is the primary factor in national security and international security for realists. They argue that wars occur because power becomes unbalanced, favoring one nation over another in such a way that the weaker nation will build arms and create alliances in order to challenge the dominance of the stronger military state it faces. If this dominant threat is one state, that state is described as a "hegemon," and its power is called "hegemonic power."

States move to establish a balance against threats, and realists say this act is the quintessential function of the state—to counter armed forces from other countries. A successful policy produces national security, which also includes the handling of similar threats internally (though in realist thinking, this component is downplayed). If one state's policymaking elites feel another coalition or state is a threat, they will counterbalance this threat by building and preparing arms and arms platforms. (Arms platforms are the media used for arms propulsion; for example, a submarine may be a platform for nuclear warheads.)

Counterbalancing states often find themselves in an arms race. In this scenario, if Nation A perceives a threat from Nation B (or another coalition) and responds by increasing its armaments, Nation B will react by augmenting its own inventory of arms. Seeing this, Nation A is confirmed in its suspicions that Nation B has a hostile intent, and it in turn further builds up its arms resources. This spiral, an arms race, is a product of the belief held by each nation that it is deterring the other from attack.

Deterrence is a part of the *para bellum* national security policy thesis. Vegetius, an ancient military strategist, posed the para bellum thesis centuries ago, which said, "If you want peace, prepare for war" (Singer 1958, 27). Preparing for war means putting together arms and troops; this very action is said to deter war because potential attackers, seeing the nation's strength and ability to fight, will not attack.

Building arms so that other countries will not attack is thought to be rational decisionmaking on the part of foreign policymakers. Rational decisions are made in favor of an action that entails more benefits than costs, and traditional national security policy is supposedly determined by assessing how much firepower is needed to make an opposing nation think it will be too costly to attack. This situation is also known as the "security dilemma" because as one country works on increasing its own deterrence, another country may respond in the same fashion, and even if no hostile intent exists between two countries, this intent can be mistaken. War may break out despite or because of their own deterrence goals.

Deterrence in ocean security means building capabilities to engage in defensive and offensive warfare on the ocean. The naval force is assembled and displayed—submarines, frigates and gunships, aircraft carriers, and large battleships. Usually, the amount of force is determined simply by the number of ships a country has and the technology it employs through them. For example, the number of nuclear-driven submarines is distinguished from the number of diesel-driven submarines because nuclear subs can generate their own energy indefinitely and stay under water for much longer periods of time. Nuclear-armed submarines are also separated from conventionally armed submarines. However, the distinction does not necessarily favor nations who possess nuclear power because those nations may be reluctant to use such devastating force. In fact, conventional weapons, such as nonnuclear missiles, may actually be more of a deterrent than nuclear weapons. International reaction to the use of a nuclear weapon would be uncertain (perhaps other nuclear powers would come to the aid of the target), and there may be no tangible benefits to be gained afterward from the targeted land or people.

International Security in the Post–Cold War Era

International security, or the preservation of peace in a global sense (not just peace for one nation), has become a counterpart to national security—the preservation of peace for a particular nation—especially since World War II. This section describes the international climate with respect to international security and provides a brief sketch of the role of the U.S. Navy.

After World War II, the United States and the Soviet Union were balanced as the global superpowers. These superpowers had command of such devastating resources and armaments, particularly nuclear bombs and later missiles, that war between them would potentially have been the end of the human race and most other life on the planet. The fact that neither country would likely survive such a war—termed *mutually assured destruction* or the *balance of terror*—created a Cold War climate in which neither side could rationally initiate war.

Much of the Cold War tension was experienced at sea. The United States had the strongest navy in the world at the end of World War II, and the Soviet Union responded by building up its naval forces and "shadowing" the U.S. fleets. Shadowing is the act of closely following the movements of a vessel, with the result that the vessel's crew is intensely aware of being under scrutiny. Due to shadowing and other close contact, U.S. and Soviet vessels had over 100 accidental collisions in this period, and given the power wielded by each country, every collision risked military escalation. In this context, escalation entails increasing military force in response to a lesser military action or casualty. From a collision, an exchange of fire may result; from an exchange of fire, more confrontations and even war may erupt.

Accordingly, the two nations recognized the importance of not setting off an accidental war between themselves, and they created a "confidence- and security-building measure" in the form of the Incidents at Sea Treaty. Confidence-building measures are efforts to reduce the risk of accidental war by establishing rules of engagement with the adversary. Such rules might include banning the pointing of guns at each other's vessels unless there is an intent to use them, providing wide berths to allow for maneuvering without collision, prohibiting "mock rammings," and even allowing representatives of each nation to visit the facilities of the other or exchanging information on one another's defense budgets from year to year. The Incidents at Sea Treaty started a trend that has many naval policymakers looking at more cooperative arrangements with regional nations.

Now that the Soviet Union has dissolved, military spending throughout the world has trended downward, except among East Asian countries (usually including Japan, China, North Korea, South Korea, Taiwan, Thailand, and Singapore). East Asia has experienced an intense arms race and an average military spending increase of nearly 40 percent since the end of the Cold War and the demise of the Soviet Union in 1991 (Lee 2000).

Commentators seem to believe this trend is a result of the United States signaling that it may be less likely to guarantee sea-lanes of control in the area as it did for its allies during the Cold War; this interpretation has been inferred from the decrease in U.S. military spending and the reduced U.S. presence in the area. Such a presence is typically referred to as a "forward presence," meaning the show of force used to extend and preserve a sphere of influence. Since the Cold War, some nations have responded to the decreased forward presence of the United States by augmenting their own naval capabilities.

The U.S. Navy

The power and extended reach of the U.S. Navy make it a notable example that can illustrate the importance of the ocean for traditional ocean security. This section will briefly describe the post–Cold War U.S. Navy.

The U.S. Navy is currently the most potent naval force in the world, and by many accounts, it is the tool with which the United States extends its global power. At this writing, there are 381,943 active-duty personnel, over 4,000 aircraft, and over 300 ships at the disposal of the U.S. Navy (U.S. Navy 2002). Among these assets, there are about 52 attack submarines, including the *Seawolf* and the new *Virginia*-class nuclear-powered subs, which are designed for search-and-destroy missions as well as for giving support to land troops through deployment of their missiles. Separate from these attack subs are the *Trident/Ohio*-class ballistic subs, which carry 50 percent of all U.S. strategic nuclear warheads. Currently, the United States has eighteen of these ballistic submarines, each carrying 24 missiles and 155 crew.

Perhaps the most powerful platforms the navy maintains are its aircraft carriers. These ships are floating air bases that can deploy fighter jets to areas in the ocean that would otherwise be inaccessible, giving the navy access to nearly any space in the world. In fact, the primary mission of the U.S. Navy's air-craft carriers is to serve as the foundation of the U.S. forward presence.

Aircraft carriers are huge and very expensive vessels. According to conservative estimates, it costs about U.S.$1.5 bil-lion annually to maintain each carrier (Morrison 1993). The United States has seven *Nimitz*-class carriers in use and two in production. The largest warships in the world, they are over 1,000 feet long and over 250 feet wide; powered by two nuclear reac-tors, they carry 85 jets, weigh about 97,000 tons, travel faster than attack submarines, and cost U.S.$4.5 billion. Carriers and the sup-port that accompanies them may be the primary military reason for post–Cold War U.S. maritime supremacy.

Without the navy, the United States would have to rely on ground bases and territorial contiguity to position its troops and weapons across the globe. This undertaking would undoubtedly be more difficult and risky than being able to send a battleship anywhere in the world. The ocean provides a reliable medium through which the United States can place its powerful armed forces; thus, just as the ocean is a geographic force that has always separated nations, it is also a force that can allow nations to con-nect to one another—for better or for worse.

During the Cold War, the U.S. Navy had the explicit mission of countering the naval threat originating from the Soviet Union and extending to Soviet-supported nations such as Cuba. Now, however, there are no clear naval rivals to the United States, and the navy's mission has changed to supporting "global stability." This means that it is used mostly as a presence to deter any action or buildup by potentially disruptive forces. The navy has prima-rily focused on the European and Asian theaters to accomplish this goal; Europe and Asia are also the most important trade areas for the United States, and the assurance of the free flow of trade is the reason why the U.S. Navy is concentrating on stability at this point.

Interestingly, the Russian Federation and other nations specifically in the Pacific have attempted to initiate further con-fidence-building measures with the U.S. Navy in the form of arms reductions, but the navy's leaders have refused to partici-pate because they continue to believe that their most effective policy is deterrence. They argue that part of deterrence is not knowing how strong your opponent is or what its intent is, and this uncertainty is a valuable tool in maintaining stability. If this uncertainty were to be compromised, they feel there would be more challengers and less stability. Of course, an essential part of deterrence is also just the opposite—that is, eliminating the uncertainty that an adversary has enough power to retaliate against an attack. Consequently, Russia and other Pacific powers have argued that this uncertainty actually provokes potential challengers and fosters instability (see Mack 1993).

Military Security: Conclusion

In sum, achieving national security is the goal of individual nation-states in relation to their counterparts. Traditionally, this has meant establishing alliances with countries and building arms as a means of balancing power internationally in response to perceived violent threats, usually from other nations. For this reason, national maritime security policy typically operates with concepts such as sea-lanes of control, spheres of influence, and deterrence as ways to protect national interests. Thus, on the ocean, much of national security is invested in national navies. International security, by contrast, has become especially focused on cooperative efforts that may limit the use of force as a way to preserve an international peace in addition to individual national peace. In regard to the ocean, international security is typically established at the bargaining table and through international pressure as well as formal and informal norms (regimes). The emerging face of ocean security, now that it has turned specifically to nonmilitary concerns, will be considered next.

Piracy

Piracy is a form of nonmilitary insecurity in that it does not arise from a breakdown in international relations but rather from the criminal violence perpetrated by private individuals and groups. Pirate activity can be a threat to the survival of the crew of cargo ships and other vessels, such as those inhabited by so-called boat people, who live on boats because they cannot afford to live on land.

Piracy is not just a subject of romantic fiction. It is a continual and well-organized violent threat to ocean security. And unfortunately, "piracy is alive and well in the modern world" (Goodman 1999, 140). It has also become modernized, with contemporary pirates having traded sailing ships and cannons for speedboats and high-tech weapons. But international cooperation against piracy has not kept pace with these developments, and trends for the crime continue to rise.

Ironically, one of the most difficult problems regarding piracy is recognizing when it has occurred. The word *piracy* is defined in international agreements as "illegal acts of violence, detention or any act of depredation . . . for private ends" in international waters (Goodman 1999, 143). According to this strict definition, piracy is something that only occurs on the high seas. Currently, antipiracy efforts reflect this strict definition and almost exclusively focus on international commercial cargo ships. This approach leaves out refugees and people who live on boats, who are often victims of murder, rape, kidnapping, theft, and assault within the jurisdictions of a nation as a result of their compromised living situations. The current definition of piracy also leaves out environmental disasters that can result when an attack is sustained against, say, a nuclear submarine for terrorist purposes (Dubner 1997).

Even if the term is narrowly defined, reports of piracy more than doubled between 1994 and 1999, and the figures are thought to underreport true occurrence rates by at least half. In 1997 alone, there were 229 cases of piracy, with over 50 deaths and more than 400 hostages taken during these attacks. Statistically, most ships are not attacked, but the increased numbers alarm officials due to the extreme violence and loss of property that is often associated with piracy.

One rising trend involves the use of "phantom ships" in the commission of fraud and theft. Phantom ships are vessels that have been hijacked, with their crews cast off or killed, and registered in a different name. The pirates sell the cargo, then take on more cargo at another port, never intending to deliver the goods. After they sell the second load, they often scrap and sell the ship itself. The *Anna Sierra*, which was flying a Cyprus flag, was at the center of one of the landmark cases in phantom shipping, as it was the first phantom ship to be found intact. In 1995, the crew of the *Anna Sierra* was attacked and cast off in lifeboats after being beaten. The ship was carrying U.S.$5 million in sugar. The master of the ship reported the crime, and two weeks later, the *Anna Sierra* was found in a Chinese port under a Honduran flag and carrying a Brazilian cargo. The ship was not returned until the owners paid Chinese officials U.S.$400,000. For some analysts, such as Jayant Abyankar, then deputy director of the International Maritime Bureau (IMB), the case confirms that China's role in phantom shipping is at the very least suspect;

Abyankar believes ports in China are regularly used to shelter hijacked vessels (Chalk 2000).

Currently, despite the rising problem of piracy, there are no international agencies working to suppress it. Each state is individually responsible for dealing with the problem. Thus, piracy suppression is not a collaborative effort in most areas, even though losses can affect a collective area when trading slows as a result. States like to control their sovereign waters absolutely, which makes cooperation for interregional law enforcement difficult. Since "most piracy occurs in territorial or internal waters," capturing pirates is in effect blocked by states who refuse international efforts to pursue them through these protected waters as a matter of upholding their own sovereignty (Gill 1996, 53). Understandably, cooperative policing efforts have been inconsistent and have had a marginal effect at best.

Cooperation in the fight against piracy has mostly occurred through partnerships of private industry and governments. The IMB is a crime-fighting division of the International Chamber of Commerce, a private organization. It receives support from the International Maritime Organization and also works with Interpol (an international network of police), both of which are public organizations. The IMB runs a piracy-reporting center in Kuala Lumpur in an effort to warn against pirate attacks. The center gathers information about piracy incidents and creates a weekly alert so that shipowners can guard against piracy in high-danger areas. In sum, however, although piracy is a growing problem, international cooperation has not significantly formed around the issue to date.

Environmental and Ecological Security

"Environmental security," another policy goal, entails stemming the *indirect* negative influences of environmental changes. Reducing the *direct* negative influences of such changes is called "ecological security." The term *indirect negative influences* refers to the concern about so-called resource wars and other disruptions of relations between states; such influences are considered indirect because the insecurity comes from the use of violence, not the environmental changes themselves. In this context, war is the security threat, not a rising sea level. The term *direct negative influences* refers to changes in the environment itself that affect the conditions of human subsistence and existence, regardless of their effect on international relations. With the acceptance of environmental change into security studies, it is now clear that the distinctions between "high security politics" and "low environmental politics" no longer apply. Both environmental and ecological security have important marine components.

Environmental security scholars appeared on the scene in the late 1970s, warning that resource degradation and population growth could lead to changes in international relations; that is, they could foster interstate and intrastate wars. The possibility that resource wars could erupt has now been acknowledged by the U.S. foreign policy establishment and the Pentagon, and averting such wars has been a policy goal since the Clinton administration.

Environmental Security

As noted earlier, the U.S. Navy is focused on maintaining global stability in order to promote and ensure global markets. Some of these markets depend directly on the ocean for their natural capital—the natural resource base on which a specific market is established. Fisheries are the natural capital stock of the fishing industry, much of which is transported across the world, and oil and natural gas reserves supply a large amount of the global hydrocarbon market. From these observations, it is logical to conclude that the resource bases themselves are vital interests for national and international security.

Two main trends are key to an understanding of why the ocean's natural resources and ecosystems are matters for security policy. One trend focuses concern on the possibility of resource wars. Traditional military policymakers, whose thinking reflects the perspective described in the preceding section on military security, have generally followed this trend. As was noted, resource wars are international and intranational (civil) wars that break out due to a dispute over a scarce resource. Ocean resource wars are mostly about fish and oil deposits. The second trend focuses on natural resource and ecosystem changes as security concerns in and of themselves. Along these lines, global warming may be considered an existential crisis: the very existence of several small island and low-lying coastal nations hangs in the balance as efforts are made to stem sea-level rise. Both trends will be examined in turn.

Resource Wars

Several security analysts believe that more wars will be fought over dwindling natural resources in the years ahead. The oceans present at least two venues in which this might be the case. The first involves competition over declining fish populations; the second involves competition over more and more scarce hydrocarbon discoveries and stores.

Before considering specific cases, the theory on which this particular concern rests should be explained. Resource wars are a legacy of Thomas Malthus, the English economist. Malthus was essentially concerned with the course of human well-being, which he believed was threatened by the startling increase in human population that he observed in England during the 1800s. He devised a model that projected the collapse of the human population based on insufficient food production. Malthus realized that population increases followed cumulative trends in which increases were often experienced in exponential terms; meanwhile, food production increases were only experienced in additive terms. Quite simply, human populations, he argued, would outpace the rate of food production, and societies would collapse from starvation and outbreaks of severe violence as a result of competition over the remaining resources. Several well-known contemporary thinkers in the United States, such as Garrett Hardin and Paul Ehrlich, followed the Malthusian model and noted that global population increases would outstrip the ability to produce sufficient food staples, especially since rising population centers were urbanizing agricultural land. Later, Nobel laureate Amartya Sen would demonstrate empirically that famines occur as a result of political disparity and poverty (the ability to gain access to food), not as a result of absolute scarcity. Nevertheless, the Malthusian model continues to be important, perhaps because the current focus on scarcity is focused not on starving masses but on the wealth that can be obtained from natural resources (which would also create an arena for intense competition).

As mentioned, the risk of a resource war involving the ocean is primarily linked to two commodities: fish and oil. Empirical data show that "the most significant issues associated with militarized disputes between democracies today concern fishing stocks, maritime boundaries, and resources of the sea, such as oil. These issues were important in over 40 percent of the ninety-seven disputes we analyzed in the post–WWII era" (Mitchell and Prins 1999).

Olav Schramm Stokke (2001, 1) wrote that "gunboat diplomacy, of course, is not a new tactic for resource management; it has been an essential part of international fisheries relations for centuries." Military force was used, for instance, to control fisheries in the "cod wars" and the "turbot war"; though no casualties were sustained in either case, it is now accepted that nations are willing to back up their demands for fish with guns. Places to watch for such conflicts include South and North Korean waters, North Korean–Chinese waters, the Mediterranean, and the Caspian Sea, to name just a few. Other places that will continue to be hot spots for ocean politics are the areas where the exclusive economic zones of one country overlap those of another to create "holes." In these areas, the economic zones come together so that there is a small space of high seas between them. Access to these spaces is guaranteed by the Law of the Sea, but the holes may be so small that they can withstand only a modest amount of fishing. The result is that pinpoint spots of concentrated fishing among declining stocks will continue to experience extreme competition between fishing fleets of various nations, and this will most likely have an effect on international relations. For example, since the fish in these holes are typically part of migratory or transboundary fish stocks, coastal nations may choose to use access to their economic zones as an incentive to get commitments from other countries to manage their activities in the holes.

Disputes related to oil may also erupt in a resource war. In 2000, the global consumption of oil was 77 million barrels a day. By 2020, this consumption is estimated to increase 43 percent, and by that time, the world is expected to have consumed two-thirds of the earth's known petroleum reserves (Klare 2001). During the 1990s, offshore oil production accounted for 25 percent of the world oil supply (Vallega 2001). Among the more important areas in the ocean for oil production are the Caspian Sea and the South China Sea—both of which are areas of high international and intranational tensions. Matters in the South China Seas have been particularly tense since 1995 when China occupied Mischief Reef, which is part of the Spratly Islands. The Spratly Islands are claimed by the Philippines, Malaysia, Vietnam, and now China. This island area may contain 100 to 150 million barrels of oil, and each of these nations have contracted with oil corporations to scout drilling areas, though work has not yet been started by any party because of the depth of the waters (Valencia 2000).

Ecological Security

Another way of viewing the environment as a security issue is to see the direct relationship between human well-being and a healthy environment. This perspective can make sense in economic and subsistence terms where natural resources provide the bases for all economies and thereby underpin the material well-being of a nation; also, natural resources provide material well-being directly, such as by producing oxygen or supplying food. According to this perspective, taking care of the ecological systems that support social systems is in itself an existential task, or one that is related to the existence or threatened existence of those social systems. Following this logic, ocean management techniques that support a growing biological community, that promote a clean and pollutant-free (to the extent possible) water environment, and that do not disturb the essential functions of the ocean are international ecological security efforts.

Among the essential functions of the World Ocean that make life possible on Earth are temperature control and stabilization and oxygen production. The currents of the ocean act as a giant climate control system that mediates Earth's warmest and coldest temperatures and keeps the planet from going too far in either direction. Unfortunately, some of these currents, including the coldest deep-ocean currents, are changing, and scientists believe this is related to global climate change. If it is true that climate change is a response to "climate forcing," or emitting pollutants into the atmosphere that force a change in the temperature of the planet, then curbing this behavior is an ecological security measure. Alterations in deep-ocean currents are but one example of how the earth's climate is believed to be changing.

The ocean also generates about 75 percent of the world's oxygen supply from plankton. Through this same component, it also allows for about 75 percent of the world's carbon sequestration, wherein carbon dioxide is traded for oxygen in the plankton. As the plankton die and float to the bottom of the ocean, the carbon dioxide they consumed does not go into the atmosphere but instead stays in them until it is released underwater. But plankton and plant life are suffering from large-scale pollution, which is affecting their function and distribution in the ocean. Temperature regulation and oxygen production are only two examples of the many connections to ocean goods and services on which life depends.

In conclusion, there are several ways in which ocean ecosystems can affect international relations. Indirectly, scarcity may produce tensions wherein the main problem becomes violence between people. Directly, environmental changes and ecosystems goods and services may present nonmilitary security threats. In either case, however, the role of conservation and rational ocean management is clear. If scarcity is a concern, conservation measures for fishing may allow some slack in the resource base and provide some time for the parties to come to a cooperative agreement. Similarly, oil consumption and competition may be decreased by conservation measures adopted in lifestyle and production. If direct environmental change is the concern, conservation efforts and ocean management become important in curbing pollution and scarcity. Ultimately, this new focus on resources as national and international security issues means that any work in the sea must treat ocean management as if it is a matter of life and death.

The Law of the Sea as Ocean Security

Since national and international security goals are at once military, economic, and resource based, the Law of the Sea is typically described as the embodiment of ocean security policy, since it addresses all of these dimensions. To some commentators, the Law of the Sea *is* ocean security; to others, it is a starting point—it is the "root stock" for future security. There are three main reasons why the Law of the Sea occupies this position. First, it is a cohesive and universal agreement that treats ocean governance and the ocean itself as a connected whole. In this way, ocean governance, security, and management are wrapped together and understood as affecting each other in important ways. Second, the Law of the Sea is one of the most widely agreed on international laws in the history of human organization. Third, the Law of the Sea has an extensive mediation component that requires nonviolent conflict resolution between the parties and the peaceful utilization of the seas. Each of these dimensions will be examined.

The Law of the Sea, as described in chapter 2, treats the oceans holistically; taken together, they form the World Ocean, which is globally connected both physically and socially to inland systems and various governance issues. Further, the Law of the Sea treats the World Ocean as a single ecosystem; as the preamble states, "The problems of ocean space are closely interrelated and must be considered as a whole" (United Nations 2001). This approach is important if ecosystem security is to be realized. It is possible within the Law of the Sea to manage ocean ecosystems as if the health of one part relied on the health of all others. The law also addresses both military and environmental security by designating rules and expectations for naval ships and environmental health.

Military security is provided in several ways. The Law of the Sea was created by nation-states just as most regimes are, and it is no surprise that the treaty gives naval ships free access to the waters of the world, with the exception of inland seas and on the temporary conditions of closing national waters to foreign warships. More important, however, is the establishment of consistent boundaries. Boundaries in the ocean are not obvious or naturally derived; instead, they must be imagined, created, and drawn up by groups of people. Consequently, prior to the third Law of the Sea convention and as the 3-mile territorial sea norm began to break down (see chapter 2), different nations had different claims and different boundary demands. The differences between nations created several militarized disputes, including the cod wars (see the related discussion later in this chapter). One of the most important functions that the 1982 Law of the Sea fulfills in international law is the setting of widely agreed on and consistent boundaries, as well as guidelines for creating and claiming new boundaries. Although several boundary conflicts persist to this day (for example, between China and North Korea), unconventional claims that demand a 200-mile territorial sea are no longer entertained. Most of the contemporary boundary conflicts actually have to do with drawing the outer limits of exclusive economic zones or with disagreements about how to divide common bays.

Environmental security is addressed by the Law of the Sea primarily in its restrictions on the mare liberum doctrine. These restrictions curb some of the international tensions between distant-water fishing nations and coastal nations, and they allow for substantive conservation measures where none existed before, internationally. Tensions between distant-water fishing nations and coastal nations are reduced by placing a determined amount of resources with the coastal nation. This may have been the most important determination in the treaty because the potential for resource wars had escalated as distant-water fishing nations were running into more and more resistance from coastal nations. For their part, coastal nations were realizing that they were losing a terrific amount of revenue and natural resources to foreign fleets, and they were not willing to stand idly by much longer.

Conservation and ecological security is served by the treaty for the same reasons. Prior to the third convention, coastal nations could not stop foreign fishing fleets from plundering their coastlines, and as a result, two important phenomena were experienced, both at the expense of the coastal ecosystem. First, because there were no rules or enforcement to which distant-water fishing fleets had to be subject, those fleets could and often did take more than a sustainable amount of fish stock. Second, because the coastal countries were witnessing their own resources being hauled off by someone else, they began to mobilize their own fleets and take the fish and other ocean goods before their competitors could. In this way, there was no community of nations guiding the use of a resource, and a tragedy of the commons (see chapter 1) scenario was experienced in several decimated fisheries. In sum, the restrictions placed on the freedom of the seas doctrine has served military and environmental security in multiple ways.

The second reason why the Law of the Sea is considered an instrument of ocean security is because there are few nations that do not abide by it. The meeting at which the treaty was negotiated was the most well attended international convention in human history at that time. The Law of the Sea also modified and limited the rule of mare liberum, which was devised by a few colonial powers and imposed from that power relationship. The alteration of this colonial legacy appealed widely to newly independent states that had recently decolonized, and this fact allowed the negotiations to take a more just and incorporative approach than was seen in previous ocean agreements. For this reason, the Law of the Sea is one of the more widely held international laws.

Finally, the Law of the Sea incorporates ocean security matters by requiring peaceful negotiations between the parties involved in conflicts related to oceans and ocean resources. It also includes a demand that the oceans be used only for peaceful purposes. In chapter 2, the mediation components were described in detail, but it is worth mentioning here that expecting peaceful resolutions is a relatively new phenomenon in international relations. This is a significant contribution for ocean security specifically. The Law of the Sea sets out rules for behavior, and there is now an international expectation and norm (an important regime) that violence should be purposefully curbed and that the rule of several international peace laws should be observed. One of these rules would be a ban on first offensives. A norm against first offensives prohibits preemptive force—in a sense, banning the use of military strikes unless they are used for self-defense in response to a prior offensive. It appears that committing a first offensive is clearly understood as unacceptable behavior (though this is difficult to know with certainly). Even powerful states that have regularly engaged in such violence now usually justify their actions by reference to a prior offense that provoked their response.

The Law of the Sea also establishes the expectation of peaceful usage, though this element of the treaty is somewhat unclear. The high seas, the exclusive economic zones, the seabed, and the seabed subsoil are said to be "reserved for the peaceful purposes." The concept of peaceful purposes may mean that nuclear weapons are banned from the area, as they are in the South Pacific. However, deterrence adherents argue that peaceful purposes may also mean the deterrence of war, which would require weapons and exercises. That being said, the convention set policy goals (albeit without definitions or mechanisms for practical application) in regard to nonviolent use of the ocean. Elisabeth Mann Borgese, who died in 2002, was one of the world's leading legal scholars on ocean governance as well as one of the most prolific writers on the topic. Some discussion on her work is key to an understanding of the future of peaceful purposes and ocean governance.

Borgese believed that the very nature of the ocean—with its physical, social, and biological properties—provides a metaphor for a different way of thinking about the world than that offered by traditional realist international law, which is built on nation-states. She called this emerging order "the oceanic circle" (a term borrowed from Mohandas Gandhi). In the oceanic circle, the World Ocean provides a way of seeing how the natural world and people are connected. Her point was that the mainstream view in Western cultures depicts the natural world and people (as well as nation-states) as individualistic. To her, this kind of thinking fostered institutions that envision a world that can be broken into parts, despite the fact that the environment and the ocean must be viewed as an interacting whole. Creating institutions such as the Law of the Sea that understand the connections not only within the natural world but between people is what she called the "barefoot revolution" or the "blue revolution" because it would happen on a grassroots level and at the level of the natural systems that exist above and below the nation-state (although that revolution would not ignore the nation-state).

Borgese developed four institutional guidelines for peaceful ocean governance. Although she believed that institutions come from people and the cultures in which they operate, she thought the institutions that the modern world has built thus far are filled with gaps and fail to solve basic problems such as overfishing and pollution. "The likely response of people to the appearance of an institutional gap is violence" (Borgese 1998, 132). Consequently, it is important, she argued, to create institutions that are (1) comprehensive, (2) consistent, (3) transsectoral or multidisciplinary, and (4) "participational." Comprehensive institutions are global institutions that "reach from the local level of the coastal community through the levels" to important global organizations. Put another way, the oceanic institutions should be "intergovernmental" in that they should allow information and decisionmaking to flow across governments of localities into global organizations.

Consistent institutions are institutions in which the decisionmaking across governments is compatible. This is a particular challenge for current international relations and ocean politics because compatible decisionmaking across governments would mean that the decisions of one government are seriously considered and mostly adhered to by other governments. Although the norms of international law are changing so that nations must consider international norms, as in the case of first offensives, nations do not regularly make decisions that are compatible with the international community—this is why there is so much trouble involved in managing common-pool resources. Regarding the ocean, it has been difficult in the past to make the resource extraction decisions of one country compatible with those of other countries so that the resource is not utterly extinguished. However, Borgese's point is that there are gaps in our current institutions that must be closed, making governments more compatible with each other, if sustainability and peace are to ever be achieved in the international community.

Borgese believed that the nature of the oceans can serve as a model for this type of governance, since the oceans' functions are diverse but ultimately compatible. Multidisciplinary institutions are institutions that use and acquire knowledge from many different sectors of inquiry. Isolated knowledge is less useful, but bringing sets and systems of knowledge together (for example, by combining physical and social sciences) also allows for a "new relationship" between science and politics. "Participational" institutions do not impose regulations on localities. Borgese argued that institutions need to bring communities into the decisionmaking process and "co-manage" resources. Again, this points to a current institutional gap because organizations often favor hierarchical structures and the accountability that goes along with this pyramid-type scheme. Typically, organizations are structured with a leader or leadership group composed of people who have increasing responsibility as they move up the ladder—in other words, they are governed from the top down. International politics are also organized this way, with the elites of a nation-state at the top, and these elites bargain and wrestle with other elites in international organizations to make international law. Local demands, needs, and desires are currently strapped to the fates of the elites that come to power within the nation-state. If local demands can make the agenda of the national elites, it is more likely that such demands will receive attention than if they do not make elite agendas.

Another gap in participation that is currently experienced stems from the fact that co-management often results in one group of people dominating the decisions, while other groups are marginalized. The regional fishery management in the United States under the Magnuson-Stevens Act is one such example. As described in chapter 2, the United States manages fisheries on a regional basis through boards that are responsible for instituting sustainable yields. However, most of the board members are from the fishing industry, and this group does not co-manage so much as it dominates the allocation of fish in this local setting. The point is that co-management is not occurring. History and politics show that human beings often have difficulty ensuring that co-management does not become subject to asymmetrical power relationships, and this institutional gap will be a major challenge to overcome. That being said, Borgese's point is that these power relationships often become institutionalized, just as in the Magnuson-Stevens Act, and as a result, rules and allocative policies are imposed on those with less power. Co-management would ultimately balance out these relationships so that those with less are given more institutional sway and those with more current power are given a handicap, a result that powerful players would be unlikely to accept without a major revolutionary turn.

The thrust of Borgese's work on international law is clear—our current institutions fall short of sustainability and peaceful governance by a wide margin. However, unlike many social scientists, Borgese went beyond deconstructing what is wrong with our current system by suggesting guidelines and goals for correcting inherent problems. Further, the four guidelines she offered for institutions can take inspiration from the ocean itself as a model that metaphorically and practically demonstrates a new mode of thinking about international ocean politics. Borgese believed that Gandhi himself was working from this model and inspiration. She quoted a poem he wrote and titled her book after it; apparently, Borgese saw the world of her dreams just as Gandhi saw the India of his:

> In this structure, composed of innumerable villages, there will be ever-widening, never ascending circles. Life will not be a pyramid with the apex sustained by the bottom. But it will be an oceanic circle whose centre will be the individual, always ready to perish for the village, the latter ready to perish for the circle of villages, till the last the whole becomes one life composed of individuals, never aggressive in their arrogance, but ever humble, sharing the majesty of the oceanic circle of which they are integral units. Therefore, the outmost circumference will not yield power to crush the inner circle but will give strength to all within and will derive its own strength from it (Gandhi 1947).

The Fishery Stock Agreement as Ocean Security

The United Nations Conference on Straddling Fish Stocks and Highly Migratory Fish Stocks (also known as the Fishery Stock Agreement, or FSA) is a side agreement of the Law of the Sea. It is now in force and will dramatically change the way ocean management deals with fishing issues. The FSA is an agreement aimed at environmental security. Since it went into force in December 2001, however, few scholars have had the opportunity to consider the influence of the FSA on ocean politics.

The FSA was negotiated in the shadow of two prominent fishing wars that demonstrated the potential for international destabilization and even conflict over fish. The agreement is meant to protect and preserve the world's high-seas fish stocks from collapsing, as a matter of ecological and commercial well-being. Consequently, the FSA is treated in this chapter as a significant addition to ocean security policy.

The Mechanics of the FSA

Through the FSA, previously unimaginable regulatory measures have now gone into force for fish that regularly travel from one national jurisdiction to another. Fish that swim these distances are called "migratory" or "straddling" stocks because they migrate or straddle international jurisdictions. The United Nations Conference on Straddling Fish Stocks and Highly Migratory Fish Stocks is the agreement set up to deal with this particular issue.

The agreement makes an unprecedented arrangement for the boarding and inspection of foreign ships to ensure compliance with conservation measures and harvesting limits. The agreement reads: "A State Party which is a member of such organization or a participant in such arrangement may, through its duly authorized inspectors, board and inspect, in accordance with paragraph 2, fishing vessels flying the flag of another State Party to this Agreement, whether or not such State Party is also a member of the organization or a participant in the arrangement" (United Nations 2002). Foreign ships will be subject to this regime even if they do not become a party to the agreement. This scheme may reduce the flags of convenience problem as it relates to fishing because every ship will be subject to the rules of the coastal region, regardless of what flag it is flying.

Protection of migratory fish as a common-pool resource is based on a commitment to the precautionary principle described in Article VI of the agreement: "States shall be more cautious when information is uncertain, unreliable or inadequate. The absence of adequate scientific information shall not be used as a reason for postponing or failing to take conservation and management measures" (United Nations 2002). In other words, protection of fish should occur even if there is not enough information to know with certainty that fish stocks are declining. In addition, the agreement takes into account biodiversity, pollution abatement, and scientific research, and it gives special consideration to developing nations, artisanal (local small-scale) fishers, and subsistence fishers. The United States has both signed and ratified this agreement, even though it is part of the Law of the Sea, which has not been ratified by the U.S. government.

The first component of the FSA relevant to ocean security is its intent to avoid resource wars. Thus, one of the major thrusts of the agreement is to institute cooperative management of fish instead of management by force. In the introductory statement to the FSA, it is noted that, among other reasons for making the treaty, negotiating parties were *"Convinced,* that an agreement relating to the implementation of the relevant provisions of the Convention would best serve these purposes [better conservation of straddling and migrating stocks] and contribute to the maintenance of international peace and security" (Hunter, Salzman, and Zaelke 2002b, 197, italics in original). One major factor for negotiating the FSA involved militarized disputes over fish, two of which deserve detailed discussion—the cod and turbot wars. In fact, the turbot war was manipulated by the Canadian government as a way to force the issue of insignificant conservation measures on the high seas in 1995. Canada had recently experienced the collapse of its cod fishery, which cost between 35,000 to 50,000 jobs (estimates differ) in Newfoundland, and legislators in that country were worried that the Greenland halibut, also known as turbot, would suffer the same fate. Turbot are found in the Grand Banks area, most of which is governed within the Canadian exclusive economic zone. However, the "nose and tail" of the Grand Banks are in international waters and beyond regulation. Consequently, the European Union rejected the quota limit suggested by Canada, set its own limit, and continued fishing turbot. In response, Canada sent warships to intervene and eventually captured a Spanish trawler outside of its economic zone; it arrested the ship's crew and displayed the nets from the ship (which were in violation of the regional fishery organization's rules) at the negotiations of the Fishery Stock Agreement in New York (Hunter, Salzman, Zaelke 2002a).

Fishing "Wars" and the FSA

Although several hundred inshore fishermen and fisherwomen have been killed in subnational conflicts with offshore trawling fleets in the Third World since the early 1970s (Fairlie 1998, 141), most violence on the sea over jurisdictions has only involved damage to property and pride. Two of the more well-known fishing jurisdiction conflicts were the cod wars and the turbot war, both of which involved loss of property and saber rattling (threats) but no casualties. The term *war* in these instances really refers to a diplomatic breakdown or, at most, a military dispute, rather than war in the usual sense of military campaigns involving battle deaths.

The cod wars began in June 1958 when, after the first UNCLOS failed to establish a larger territorial sea, the Icelandic government declared a 12-mile zone around its coasts. This action was clearly a violation of international legal expectations of the time, but the Icelandic fisheries were being depleted quickly by foreign trawlers. Also, local fish exporters relied on the coastal fisheries for 80 to 90 percent of their exports (Juda 1996, 172). In conjunction with this local pressure, Great Britain heavily relied on the Icelandic fisheries, where it caught 20 percent of all its fish and where most of the catch was cod. When Iceland attempted to enforce its national jurisdiction, the British navy arrived and occasionally rammed Icelandic coast guard vessels. Eventually, Britain and Iceland settled the matter in an agreement that phased in a 12-mile fishery zone over three years. However, it was not until UNCLOS-III that the matter was totally resolved and the 12-mile territorial sea permanently established.

The turbot war occurred between Canada and Spain on March 9, 1995. On that day, a Canadian coast guard boat fired shots across the bow of the Spanish trawler *Estai* before confiscating the vessel for fishing turbot, a straddling species, just outside the Canadian EEZ. Spain protested because Canada took these actions *beyond* its 200-mile economic zone, an undisputed fact. Canadians continued to chase Spanish fishers from that area of the Grand Banks, and Spain took Canada to the International Court of Justice over the matter, despite a settlement in April 1995.

Was the seizing of the Spanish boat an act of piracy? The Canadians defended their actions under their own law, which "authorized [Canada] to enforce fishing regulations 'beyond [its] own 200-mile limits into the so-called straddling areas,'" as stipulated in the Canadian Coastal Fisheries Protection Act amended in 1994 (Faith 1996, 206). However, states cannot make laws that violate international ones and still say they are in compliance with the international law. Even though Article 117 of UNCLOS stipulates that states are supposed to cooperate with one another in conservation measures, Canada's conservation intentions were only made known nationally, and the Spanish fishers had no obligation to abide by them outside the Canadian EEZ. The turbot war was concluded when a bilateral agreement between Canada and Spain was forged that lowered the total turbot catch for Canada and raised the catch for Spain in the Grand Banks fishing area. Since the area was international waters, the bilateral agreement had to be recognized by other countries, which was done when 100 delegates signed the settlement.

The effect of the conflict was not lost on the delegates to the FSA. It was clear that national economies were at stake and that fish wars could become a factor if high-seas fishing was not regulated. It is for this reason that the FSA became the first global instrument to allow for an enforceable limit on the freedom to restrict fishing on the high seas.

Ecological Security and the FSA

A Canadian report issued in response to the Atlantic cod declines noted, "Failure of the [groundfish] resource means a calamity that threatens the existence of many of these communities throughout Canada's Atlantic coast, and the collapse of a whole society. . . . We are dealing here with a famine of biblical scale—a great destruction" (Rogers 1995, 84–85). The FSA agreement realizes the huge importance of fish, and it links the health of fisheries to human security.

Protection for the biological community and the people who depend directly on fish locally and regionally is now enforceable. The precautionary principle is used as the organizational foundation and basis for decisionmaking in the FSA. As the Atlantic cod fishery was collapsing, the Bering Sea pollack fishery was also being decimated. The Bering Sea is an area with a hole, as described earlier; the economic zones of Russia and the United States completely surround the "Donut Hole" where several nations fish for pollack, the primary source for frozen fish products and fast-food fish sandwiches. In 1989, this fishery yielded 1.4 million tons of pollack, but by 1994, it had collapsed to a yield of 10,000 tons, a reduction of more than 99.999 percent; further, this collapse did not result from use of the whole fishery but only from the 3 percent (the Donut Hole area) that was in high seas (Hunter, Salzman, Zaelke 2002a). The pollack and the people who required income from fishing them had suffered from an absence of regulation because the fish were beyond the national control of any one country, leaving the fishery open for everyone to take as much as they could before others did the same. Eventually, a multilateral treaty was signed for the Bering Sea fishery, and the development of this treaty provided guidelines for the simultaneous development of the FSA. Beyond simple economic resource conservation plans, the FSA is a direct link to ocean management *as* ocean security, wherein preserving the biological communities in the ocean focuses on taking care of social systems as much as taking care of the ecosystem.

Conclusion and Suggestions for the Future

In conclusion, it is clear that ocean politics is fraught with insecurity. Nation-states often function as centralized organizations that are well armed and ambitious. On the oceans, control of traffic and access is vital to commerce and affluence, and European colonial powers and contemporary U.S. hegemony provide strong examples of how much power can be accumulated through maritime supremacy.

The application of national power through the use of armed force is now being placed within the context of environmental security. U.S. foreign policy has incorporated the notion of resource wars into its military strategy. Further, environmental functions of the ocean are at a critical juncture at this point in history; if some ecological functions are altered further, the quality of life on the planet will be compromised. The following are suggestions for the various categories of ocean security policy that may help to avert disaster.

Military Security

Military security policy is typically divided into two categories: policy that deals with nuclear technology and policy that does not. Policies that may help avoid war involving nuclear technology will be discussed first.

The Cold War is over, but a powerful legacy of this tense nuclear age remains in the form of nuclear weapons and nuclear-powered warships. Within this policy area, there are several levels of concern, ranging from the mining of nuclear fuel, such as uranium, to the use and disposal of nuclear weapons and wastes. Mining for nuclear fuel in the ocean has not yet become an issue. The use of nuclear weapons and the waste resulting from production and postproduction activity connected with these weapons thus become the focus of marine nuclear military security.

Like terrestrial uses of nuclear weapons, marine nuclear missiles (such as the U.S.-built *Trident* missiles) are less strategic than conventional weapons. This means that these missiles offer fewer policy options than conventional weapons, simply due to their comprehensive destructive force. The building of a nuclear arsenal is, of course, planned on the basis of deterrence, but if the decision to use the weapons is made, ultimate human and environmental destruction is a possible result. Consequently, nuclear arsenals do not have the same persuasiveness in terms of policy that conventional weapons have because an adversary knows that a higher threshold must be crossed before deciding to use nuclear weapons. Unlike conventional weapons, nuclear weapons cannot be used for a short time and then backed off, while waiting for negotiations to occur. There are, to be sure, some smaller nuclear weapons that have more tactical applications, but their use still offers fewer options than the use of regular munitions.

On the ocean, the platforms for such weapons are submarines or other warships. It would be idealistic to say that nuclear weapons should simply be banned, since the countries that have them will not likely give them all up and the countries that do not have them may continue to want them. Therefore, the primary policy suggestion is to keep this area of international negotiations open and active. Lists of arsenals should be made transparent to any citizen or nation (this policy is in harmony with notions of deterrence, since knowledge of capabilities is necessary in order to calculate what it will take to avoid war). International inspectors should be allowed to inspect all arms and weapons, and discussions of the world's nuclear weapons should not cease just because the Cold War is over.

Nuclear power on the ocean is perhaps an equally important threat. Nuclear weapons are benign if they are not used, but the nuclear power plants aboard naval vessels, mostly belonging to the United States and the Soviet Union/Russia, have the potential to do a great deal of damage to the ocean. At present, there are at least fifty nuclear weapons and twenty-three nuclear reactors on the bottom of different seas, some of which still contain "hot" fuel (Broadus and Vartanov 1994). Beyond that, the Soviet Union/Russia has been dumping nuclear waste into the Sea of Japan since the 1950s, and as late as 1993, it dumped 900 tons of low-level liquid nuclear waste into that body. From the 1960s until 1986, the Soviet Union may have dumped as many as 17,000 containers of both liquid and solid nuclear waste into the Barents and Kara Seas, despite the fact that the Soviet Union signed the London Dumping Convention, which banned nuclear waste dumping in the ocean in 1983 (Morioka 1997).

Since saltwater corrodes the encasements of the power plants, radiation from these plants is contaminating several areas. Marine life in the Sea of Japan is now feared to be affected by this radiation. Furthermore, Russian-Japanese relations, which have a violent history to begin with, are stressed further by this pollution. The policy here is simple: decommissioned nuclear-driven vessels should not be allowed to be dumped into the ocean. The ocean is not the infinite sink it was once thought to be, and such nuclear contamination affects a delicate web of ecological relationships. Also, nations that have nuclear-driven fleets should not be allowed to trade their waste to poor countries that have less capacity to deal with the contamination than wealthier nations. Often, waste-trading funds are not applied to protective measures in order to preserve revenue, and poorer countries end up exposing their citizens to material for which they gained no benefit in the first place. Keeping nuclear waste out of the oceans and with the countries that originated and benefited from it is also a good way for nations and communities to be more tied to the high costs of nuclear technology; these costs should not be transferred to foreign governments or to other generations by hiding the waste in the ocean.

Conventional maritime military security is also in a difficult position. Deterrence by the accumulation of conventional weapons is shown to actually increase the probability of the very violence it is meant to deter. For this reason, deterrence is not a particularly desirable policy goal (on land or on sea) if the ultimate goal is an absence of violence. For a greater "peace dividend," there are several alternatives to deterrence theory. One is increased confidence-building measures and arms reductions, discussed earlier in this chapter. Another is the increased use of "collective security" schemes.

Collective security schemes are increasingly being used for geographic regions with cultural and economic ties. People of these regions realize that individual action is not going to solve problems that they experience collectively. By pooling their resources, they can enhance their military capabilities. The result is that this effort seems to displace the realist suspicion that any neighbor might be the next aggressor. It also promotes more openness and communication between the regional states, which then have a more accurate understanding of the hostility level of their neighbors. Since hostility is usually understood as intentions multiplied by capabilities, if it is known that a neighbor has no malicious intent, its hostility potential is zero; such an assessment is difficult to ascertain under traditional realist deterrence operations, which discount collective security schemes as an elective tool for maintaining peace. Pooling military capacity in geographic regions is also being recognized as an increasing need for ocean policing. Specifically, several military analysts have called for collective navies to patrol common-pool fisheries and for the United Nations to maintain a standing global navy. Were the latter to occur, the capacity of the United Nations would probably expand exponentially, given the importance of access and control of the oceans to a global power arrangement. Unfortunately, no one is really sure how to abate international violence and war, but collective arrangements probably can have some utility in enlarging the global peace dividend.

Piracy

Piracy is only a statistical inconvenience when compared to global traffic on the ocean, but it can be particularly violent and have devastating effects on life and property. Two suggestions come to mind in dealing with piracy. The first is to create a definition of piracy that includes (and takes note of) broader acts of violence on the sea as well as purposeful acts meant to injure the marine environment. Good definitions are important to good policy because they outline what is and what is not considered. Certain important aspects of marine violence are currently being ignored. Second, as Timothy Goodman (1999) suggested, nations may be able to control piracy regionally through charters that incorporate national enforcement agreements and establish joint patrol responsibilities to disperse the costs of enforcement over an entire area. This area may benefit from an international conference that should be organized by the International Maritime Organization. Finally, people living in poverty on boats need additional political power and protection from the often brutal violence they suffer, if their rights and safety are to be secured. One possibility is to make the United Nations responsible for the boat people. When refugees are known to be accumulating in an area, the United Nations sends observers and organizes aid; refugee treaties offer baseline treatment standards for refugees, and people living on boats may be helped by receiving similar attention.

Environmental Security

Environmental security policy options are divided into two problem categories but seem to have mutual solutions. First, resource wars apparently occur for several reasons, and these causes should be stemmed when possible. One cause is scarcity. Quite often, scarcity can be averted with interdisciplinary, participatory resource management and conservation. Another cause is relative market value (oil, for example, is very valuable even if there is some disagreement about its scarcity). A high market value of a resource such as oil provides an incentive for nations to attempt to control that resource, which is probably why the Pentagon is the policy community that directs U.S. environmental security initiatives. However, if the goal is to avoid violence over a resource in an unstable area, such as the Caspian Sea, then sharing arrangements along with collective defense responsibilities may provide an answer. In the Caspian, for instance, perhaps Russian and other Caspian littoral states can create a defense community to guarantee the security of oil extracted from the sea while sharing the revenues that result from this protection.

Ecological security needs also require active management and conservation. That is the underlying message of this whole book—active management of ocean resources is needed to prevent overexploitation and damage if these same ocean resources are expected to provide continuing support, subsistence, goods, and services to the human race. In the most simplistic terms, taking care of oceanic resources ensures that these resources can take care of us. Under this premise, the relationship between ecology and human society is reciprocal; efforts to dominate nature for short-term benefit, as has been seen in the Grand Banks, the Bering Sea, and numerous other places, only increases the level of ecological insecurity. Consequently, one policy suggestion is to continue to reinforce this dependence publicly via policy statements and goals, along with action plans that measure economic goals against their ecological consequences. Ultimately, social and natural scientists must develop policy that does not favor "the economic question" and that gives equal (or greater) weight to ecological concerns. Currently, economic concerns have primacy in policymaking. Economic primacy seems to operate under the assumption that corporate, multinational economic health should be the first consideration, with ecological consequences being secondary. Such an approach is not in the long-term best interest of the oceans or the humans that depend on them for life support. Ocean policy analysts should not back away from this challenge but continue to work on the dynamics of our economic and ecological system relationships.

References

Borgese, Elisabeth Mann. 1998. *The Oceanic Circle: Governing the Seas as a Global Resource*. New York: United Nations University Press.

Broadus, James, and Raphael Vartanov. 1994. *The Oceans and Environmental Security: Shared U.S. and Russian Perspectives*. Washington, DC: Island Press.

Chalk, Peter. 2000. *Non-military Security and Global Order: The Impact of Extremism, Violence and Chaos on National and International Security*. New York: St. Martin's Press.

Dubner, Barry Hart. 1997. "Human Rights and Environmental Disaster: Two Problems That Defy the 'Norms' of the International Law of Sea Piracy." *Syracuse Journal of International Law and Commerce* 23, no. 1: 1–65.

Fairlie, Simon. 1998. "Fisheries: Confrontation and Violence in the Management of Marine Resources." In Mohamed Suliman, ed., *Ecology, Politics and Violent Conflict*. New York: Zed Books.

Faith, Jeremy. 1996. "Enforcement of Fishing Regulations in International Waters—Piracy or Protection: Is Gunboat Diplomacy the Only Means Left?" *Loyola of Los Angeles International and Comparative Law Journal* 19: 199–221.

Gandhi, Mohandas. 1947. *India of My Dreams*. Bombay: Hind Kitabs.

Gill, Martin. 1996. "Security at Sea: Fraud, Piracy and the Failure of Police Cooperation Internationally." *International Relations* 13, no. 3: 43–58.

Goodman, Timothy. 1999. "'Leaving the Corsair's Name to Other Times': How to Enforce the Law of Sea Piracy in the 21st Century through Regional International Agreements." *Case Western Reserve Journal of International Law* 31, no. 107: 139–168.

Hunter, David, James Salzman, and Durwood Zaelke. 2002a. *International Environmental Law and Policy*, 2nd ed. New York: Foundation Press.

———. 2002b. *International Environmental Law and Policy*, 2nd ed., Treaty Supplement. New York: Foundation Press.

Juda, Lawrence. 1996. *International Law and Ocean Use Management: The Evolution of Ocean Governance*. New York: Routledge.

Klare, Michael. 2001. *Resource Wars: The New Landscape of Global Conflict*. New York: Metropolitan Books.

Lee, Choon Kun. 2000. "Seapower and Security at the Close of the Twentieth Century." In Dick Wilson and Dick Sherman, eds., *Oceans Governance and Maritime Strategy*. St Leonards, New South Wales, Australia: Allen and Unwin Publishers.

Mack, Andrew, ed. 1993. *A Peaceful Ocean? Maritime Security in the Pacific in the Post–Cold War Era*. St Leonards, New South Wales, Australia: Allen and Unwin Publishers, copyrighted under the Berne Convention.

Midlarsky, Manus. 1995. "Environmental Influences on Democracy: Aridity, Warfare and a Reversal of the Casual Arrow." *Journal of Conflict Resolution* 37, no. 4: 1207–1230.

Mitchell, Sara McLaughlin, and Brandon Prins. 1999. "Beyond Territorial Integrity: Issues at Stake in Democratic Militarized Interstate Disputes." *International Studies Quarterly* 43, no. 1: 178–179.

Morioka, Takashi. 1997. "Japan Sea Contamination." *Trade and Environment Database*. Available online at http://www.american.edu/TED/JAPANSEA.HTM. Accessed November 20, 2002.

Morrison, David. 1993. "How Many Carriers Are Enough?" *National Journal* 25, no. 36: 2162.

Padfield, Peter. 2000. *Maritime Supremacy and the Opening of the Western Mind: Naval Campaigns That Shaped the Modern World*. New York: Overlook Press.

Pew Oceans Commission. 2001. *Marine Pollution in the United States*. Arlington, VA: Pew Oceans Commission.

Rogers, Raymond. 1995. *The Oceans Are Emptying: Fish Wars and Sustainability*. New York: Black Rose Books.

Singer, David. 1958. "Threat Perception and the Armament-Tension Dilemma." *Journal of Conflict Resolution* 2, no. 1: 90–105.

Stokke, Olav Schram, ed. 2001. *Governing the High Seas Fisheries: The Interplay of Global and Regional Regimes*. Oxford: Oxford University Press.

United Nations. 2001. *United Nations Conference on the Law of the Sea*. Available online at http://www.un.org/Depts/los/index.htm. Accessed November 20, 2002.

———. 2002. "The United Nations Agreement for the Implementation of the Provisions of the United Nations Convention on the Law of the Sea of 10 December 1982 Relating to the Conservation and Management of Straddling Fish Stocks and Highly Migratory Fish Stocks." Available online at http://www.un.org/Depts/los/convention_agreements/convention_overview_fish_stocks.htm. Accessed on November 20, 2002.

U.S. Navy. 2002. "The Status of the Navy." Available online at http://www.navy.mil/. Accessed May 13, 2002.

Valencia, Mark. 2000. "Energy Resources and Security in Asia-Pacific." In Dick Wilson and Dick Sherman, eds., *Oceans Governance and Maritime Strategy*. St Leonards, New South Wales, Australia: Allen and Unwin Publishers.

Vallega, Adalberto. 2001. *Sustainable Ocean Governance: A Geographical Perspective*. New York: Routledge.

4

Chronology

Events in ocean management span many disciplines, including oceanography, naval history, biology, politics, and law. This chronology is meant to delineate the progress (or lack thereof) in ocean-related concepts and governance. The entries in this and the following chapter have been chosen for their impact on the World Ocean and on ocean politics, broadly speaking.

Some discoveries and ideas, despite their long histories, receive little attention in policy. The idea that life on Earth began in the ocean, for example, seems largely irrelevant to policymakers. And as policy and political arguments circle around separate and seemingly unrelated issues, the primal dependence that the planet and all its life forms have on the ocean is all too often forgotten or simply ignored.

Early Ocean Hallmarks

3.2–4 billion years ago   Microscopic life on the planet begins in the oceans.

550 million years ago   The "biologist's big bang," called the Cambrian explosion, occurs in the World Ocean. The explosion of life in this era unveils the major patterns and forms of life to come.

65 million Modern life on the planet emerges from the ocean.
years ago

450 B.C.   Herodotus establishes a study of tides and silt in the Nile Delta and coins the term *Atlantic* to describe the seas to the west of Greece.

322 B.C.   Aristotle passes away. Besides his famous philosophical treatises, he is known as the "Father of Natural History." He devises and records a scientific method, names and describes many marine animals, and correctly identifies cetaceans (porpoises, whales, and so on) as mammals.

100   The earliest whaling begins in what would become Japan.

800   Norwegian, French, and Spanish whaling begins (Andresen 1998, 433).

1000   Magnetic compasses are widely used by Chinese mariners (Borgese 1998, 26).

Vikings sail along the northeastern seaboard of America.

1275   Europe creates its first sea chart, the Carta Pisana, about four hundred years after the Chinese had constructed similar maps.

1340   The English win the Battle of Sluys, taking control of the English Channel from the French in the opening of the Hundred Years' War.

Early 1400s   Henry the Navigator, "Infante of Portugal," founds an interdisciplinary and international oceanographic institute with scholars from Italy, Spain, Arab countries, and Portugal. The institute develops charts and navigational equipment. Based near Sagres, Portugal, it spawns a wave of seafaring colonial explorers who were students at the school. These explorers included Christopher Columbus, Gil Eanes, and Vasco da Gama (Borgese 1998).

1494   Spain and Portugal sign the Treaty of Tordesillas, which divides all the world's oceans between these two countries. This move is viewed by other nations as a strategic attempt to restrict trade, and it eventually culminates in the famous Dutch response from Hugo Grotius (see 1609).

1519   Magellan starts out on his voyage to circumnavigate the globe and provides the first navigational proof that the earth is round.

1542   Spanish navigators discover the North Equatorial Current of the Pacific Ocean (Deacon 1997).

1609   Hugo Grotius anonymously publishes *Mare Liberum*. Some authorities record this date as 1608. *Mare Liberum* establishes the "freedom of the seas" doctrine, which sets the tone for universal and free access to the ocean for almost four hundred years (see chapters 2 and 5).

    Johannes Kepler publishes *Atronomia Nova seu de Motu Stallae Martis,* in which he explains that tides are a result of gravitational attraction from the moon. This explanation is still considered accurate. At the same time, Galileo dismisses the idea in favor of his notion that the earth's rotation causes the changes in tide levels (Deacon 1997).

1663   Robert Hooke, a British member of the Royal Society (still the oldest existing scientific organization), reveals his invention of a water barometer. This barometer is able to measure water pressure, albeit within serious limits. The tool is used to measure ocean depth; it proves more accurate than the previous technique of dropping a tethered weight to the bottom.

1665   Robert Boyle, whose main contribution to science is a law on gases (which holds that the volume of gas varies according to pressure), publishes a work in which he determines that the bottom depths of the ocean are always cold. This knowledge will influence the way currents and subsequently global thermal regulation are understood.

1712   American colonists begin hunting sperm whales.

1731   The sextant is invented independently in England by mathematician John Hadley and in America by Thomas Godfrey (Electric Library 2000). The sextant measures up to 120 degrees by lining up stars and the horizon through an angled viewer; mariners navigating the high seas find it very useful for measuring distances.

1759   John Harrison invents the first chronometer, which allows navigators to determine longitude while at sea.

1768   Stellar's sea cow, which resembles a large manatee, becomes extinct only twenty-seven years after being discovered by Western scientists (Becher 1998).

1769   Benjamin Franklin publishes his first map of the Gulf Stream, which proves to be remarkably accurate.

1776   James Watt develops a steam engine. Steam-powered boats emerge twenty-five years later.

1786   The Pribiloff Islands are discovered. The area is a base for millions of fur seals that are hunted for the fur trade.

1793   The semaphore signaling system is developed by Claude Chappe. The system uses two handheld flags that are moved into different positions to communicate alphanumeric signals. This system is useful to seafarers trying to communicate with other visible but distant ships.

1803   Robert Fulton builds the first submarine.

1819   The *Savanah* becomes the first steamship to cross the Atlantic.

1821   The first oceangoing iron-hulled ship is built.

1828   J. Vaughan Thomson is the first to describe planktonic stages of crabs, though the word *plankton* is not used until Joseph Hooker coins the term (see 1847).

1830s   The first fishing trawlers (boats that pull large nets behind them) emerge, allowing for much larger catches at one time than prior methods.

1831   Charles Darwin sets out on his famous scientific voyage aboard the HMS *Beagle*. He is known as the father of evolutionary theory, which he developed by visiting the Galapagos Islands. These islands are now an international reserve largely due to Darwin's work in detailing species endemic (uniquely indigenous) to that archipelago (set of islands). His mission is completed in 1836.

1837   Samuel Morse invents a telegraph communications system and the Morse code, which become an important part of transoceanic communication.

1839   France and Great Britain agree to adhere to rules regarding 3-mile territorial seas, ending a debate that had lasted since Hugo Grotius's time as to how far the territorial area should extend.

1841   Edward Forbes, claimed by some to be the first modern oceanographer (Matthew Fontaine Maury competes for this title as well—see chapter 5), sails on the British survey ship the *Beacon*. Dredging the Aegean and Mediterranean Seas at previously untouched depths of 300 fathoms (about 1,800 feet), Forbes uses this opportunity to promote his belief that the bottom ocean depths are lifeless (azoic). His azoic theory, however, will later be proved patently false.

1847   Joseph Hooker identifies planktonic diatoms (Bacillariophyta, or single-celled algae) as plants that exchange carbon dioxide for oxygen. It is now known that phytoplankton, or the whole range of microscopic drifting algae, supply most (about 75 percent) of the oxygen for the whole planet, not just the ocean.

1851   The first undersea cable connects the European continent to Great Britain.

1855   Matthew Fontaine Maury, considered by some a father of oceanography, publishes the discipline's first textbook, *The Physical Geography of the Sea.*

1858   Geographer Antonio Snider-Pelligrini creates a map that illustrates how the continents could have fit together in the distant past. This map becomes the first piece of evidence for plate tectonics.

1865   The scientist James Bertram publishes *The Harvest of the Sea,* which sounds one of the first warnings that ocean fisheries are not as plentiful as previously thought.

1867   The United States purchases Alaska and the associated Aleutian and Pribiloff Islands for $7.2 million, which touches off indiscriminate and large hunts that quickly devastate the population of seals that use these islands (see chapter 1).

1869   The Suez Canal opens, connecting the Mediterranean and Red Seas.

1872   The crewmen of the HMS *Challenger* set out to discover all that they can about the marine world. They will document 4,017 new species and discover polymetallic nodules at the bottom of the ocean. The mission is completed in 1876.

1873   *Challenger* leader Charles Wyville Thomson publishes a major text in oceanography, *The Depths of the Sea.*

        Louis Agassiz establishes the Anderson School, the first U.S. marine biological laboratory. This laboratory will later become the largest private oceanographic research facility in the world, known today as the Woods Hole Oceanographic Institute (see chapter 8).

1883   Renowned scientist T. H. Huxley opens the Great International Fisheries Exhibition in London with a keynote address arguing that human efforts could not affect the vast amount of fish in the ocean.

1885   A British report indicates fisheries are in decline across several areas in British territorial waters.

The first modern oil tanker, the *Gluckauf*, is launched from northern England. The tanker revolutionizes petroleum transportation by storing oil in its own cargo holds instead of separate barrels.

1889   The British Parliament adopts the Sea Fisheries Act and Herring Fisheries Act to protect Moray Firth, a semienclosed sea, from otter trawlers because they are suspected of causing a decline in the area's herring population. The acts are effective *beyond* the 3-mile limit and attract international protest.

1892   The United States and Great Britain sign the Treaty of Washington to solve the problem of the overhunting of seals in the Bering Sea.

1893   A committee of the British Parliament concludes that fisheries in the North Sea are obviously declining.

1899   The U.S. Congress passes the Rivers and Harbors Act, which regulates oil discharges from ships but only to the extent that they impede navigation.

Modern Ocean Hallmarks: The Past 100 Years

1902   King Oscar II of Sweden establishes the International Council for the Exploration of the Sea (ICES). Today, ICES is the oldest intergovernmental science organization in the world and operates under a formal international treaty created in 1964.

1903   Panama and the United States sign a treaty to allow the United States to begin building the Panama Canal. The canal cuts through Panama to eliminate the trip around South America for ships making coast-to-coast voyages. The United States purchases the rights to the

1903
(cont.)

land from France for U.S.$40 million. The canal is finished and the first ship passes through it in August 1914.

1904

Japan begins pelagic, or open-ocean, whaling in the Antarctic.

1907

The Hague Peace Conference determines rules for laying mines in the ocean. Among other stipulations, the conference demands that the mines should be recoverable when they are no longer needed. This conference still stands as the only international agreement on undersea mines (Dimitrov 1992).

1909

The *Carnegie* sets out on its maiden voyage. It is the first nonmagnetic science brigantine to be built for the purpose of mapping magnetic geological areas of the ocean. There is no iron on any part of the ship or crew so as not to disturb the instruments. Later, the ship catches fire and burns in an accident in Samoa.

1911

The North Pacific Sealing Convention is signed by the United States, Great Britain, Russia, and Japan to limit the overhunting of seals in the Bering Sea (see chapter 1).

The first diesel-powered ship crosses the Atlantic, fourteen years after Rudolf Diesel's invention of an engine that uses oil as fuel.

1912

On the night of April 14–15, the RMS *Titanic* strikes an iceberg and sinks, and over 1,500 people lose their lives. (RMS stands for Royal Mail Ship; thus, the *Titanic* could deliver British mail. Another designation—HMS, short for His Majesty's Ship—is typically applied to British warships but is sometimes incorrectly used in regard to the *Titanic*.) As a result of this accident, the first of several international conventions on safety at sea is held two years later to improve safety equipment as well as navigational and rescue gear standards on ships (International Maritime Organization 2001).

1913   Johan Hjort, a Norwegian zoologist, receives the Alexander Agassiz Medal for distinguished work in oceanography. Hjort's work shows that the amount of plankton available for young fish determines the strength of that *year class*, Hjort's term to classify fish of each species born in a year (see chapter 5).

1914   Reginald Fessenden, a former assistant to Thomas Edison, invents the first sonar device; it is intended to detect icebergs but will also be employed to detect submarines during World War I.

1915   On May 7, during World War I, the British ocean liner *Lusitania* is sunk by a German submarine, resulting in the death of 1,190 people (see chapter 5).

Alfred Wegener publishes his first edition of *The Origins of Continents and Oceans*. Wegener offers the first portion of the plate tectonics theory by arguing that all the continents were once a single mass (called "Pangea") that later broke apart. Wegener supports his theory by uncovering similar fossils in different continents. Since the continents presumably drifted away from each other, the theory is called "continental drift" and is still accepted today (Prager 2000).

1922   In a joint resolution, the U.S. Congress indicates its first concerns over oil pollution caused by ships. Later in the year, serious oil pollution is recognized as an indisputable problem that is also correlated with declining fisheries and other marine life.

1924   The U.S. Congress passes the Oil Protection Act of 1924, which regulates the discharge of oil from ships.

The United States and Great Britain, on behalf of Canada, create an unprecedented treaty to restrict halibut fishing in their own territorial waters. The agreement is designed to address the decade-long decline of halibut populations.

The Scripps Institution of Oceanography is established in La Jolla, California. The institution originates

1924   from a research foundation created by William Ritter
(cont.)   nineteen years earlier. Ritter was a student of Louis
          Agassiz, who started what would become the Woods
          Hole Oceanographic Institute (see 1873).

1925   The *Meteor* begins a two-year expedition. The crew of
          this German naval ship completes the first modern
          oceanographic research, measuring salinity, ocean
          temperatures, plankton, and atmosphere.

1926   The International Law Association adopts a draft con-
          vention that gives the coastal state jurisdiction over
          the seabed in territorial waters. This is the first move
          to establish a complete "water column" jurisdiction.
          The water column divides the ocean into parts: the
          seabed/subsea floor (benthic zone), the ocean water
          (pelagic zone), and the airspace above.

          The International Washington Conference meets to
          regulate oil discharges on the high seas but fails to
          establish a regime due to concerns about limiting the
          freedom of the seas.

1928   The American Society of Mammologists urges the
          international community to address the wasteful pro-
          cedures of whale hunting and calls for a conservation
          scheme to address the declining numbers of whales.

1930   The Woods Hole Oceanographic Institute is founded
          to conduct independent, private oceanographic
          research in Massachusetts. The institute becomes a
          leader in marine science (see 1873 and chapter 8).

          The League of Nations holds the Conference for the
          Codification of International Law at The Hague. This
          conference foreshadows the first Law of the Sea con-
          vention by debating (albeit inconclusively) territorial
          sea parameters and exclusive fishery zones (Glassner
          1990, 4).

          In March, Mohandas Gandhi starts his 200-mile trek
          from Ahmedabad, India, to the Arabian Sea; it is
          known as the Salt March or Salt Protest. The goal of

this march is to take control of everyday resources from the British Empire and restore it to Indian villagers. Gandhi walks to the sea to protest English colonization as well as the British monopoly of one of the ocean's most plentiful natural resources, salt. Gandhi's efforts are focused on Indians using things around them to be self-sufficient, and he demonstrates that the ocean can serve even the poorest citizen in very basic ways. Hundreds of Indians are beaten at a salt factory when they engage in nonviolent protest by lining up to take over this facility (Erikson 1969).

1934   Zoologists William Beebe and Otis Barton are the first people to view deep-sea environments. They use a submersible that is tethered to a ship and reach a depth of 923 meters (3,072 feet).

1939   World War II erupts in Europe. As a result, fisheries in the Northern Hemisphere get a respite from intensive fishing. The lull in fishing consequently rejuvenates fisheries for several years.

1945   On September 28, U.S. president Harry Truman declares jurisdiction and control of the U.S. continental shelf and U.S. coastal fisheries beyond the territorial seas where "prior interest" had been established (areas where the United States had been fishing prior to the declaration). This move eventually spurs the international community to convene the Law of the Sea conventions.

1946   The burgeoning whaling industry, which had peaked in 1931, forces whaling nations to adopt the International Convention for the Regulation of Whaling (Andresen 1998, 433). At first, this convention only limits the taking of certain species and mothers with calves and the wasting of too much of the carcasses. Later, a full commercial ban on whaling will be adopted.

1948   The International Maritime Consultancy Organization (IMCO) is created to handle technical problems of international shipping. The IMCO later becomes the International Maritime Organization (IMO).

1948
(cont.)

The International Whaling Commission is created by the International Convention for the Regulation of Whaling to handle the large whaling industry and falling whale stocks (Andresen 1998).

1952

Chile, Ecuador, and Peru issue the Santiago Declaration, which proclaims a territorial zone of 200 miles from their coasts. The countries cite the need to protect their food supplies and economic development as the main reasons for the declaration.

1954

The London Oil Pollution Convention convenes to negotiate the first international oil pollution regime and later adopts the International Convention for the Prevention of Pollution of the Sea by Oil (OILPOL). The main purpose of this convention is to regulate purposeful oil pollution by tankers (see chapter 2).

The first nuclear-powered submarine is commissioned. The USS *Nautilus* introduces a new generation of subs that use onboard nuclear power plants to drive and operate the ships' systems. The Soviet Union builds its first nuclear sub in 1958, something the United Kingdom will not accomplish until 1963 with the HMS *Dreadnought*. France, China, and India soon follow suit.

1956

The Suez Canal temporarily closes as the British relinquish control to Egypt under pressure of Egyptian riots. The canal is a source of international conflict as French, British, and Israeli troops fight Egypt over the next ten years. During the Arab-Israeli War of 1967, the canal is closed to prevent Israeli ships from passing. Some newly built ships, especially oil supertankers, are too large to pass through the canal anyway, and the use of the canal becomes less important to ocean shipping.

1958

The United Nations Convention on the Law of the Sea meets for the first time (UNCLOS-I) to establish a modern ocean law that would revise the freedom of the seas doctrine.

After participants in UNCLOS-I fail to agree on a wider territorial sea limit, Iceland declares a 12-mile exclusive zone to protect its cod fishery from British trawlers. Britain decries the move and occasionally rams Icelandic coast guard ships as a result (see chapter 3).

1959   The Antarctic Treaty is signed in Washington, D.C., by twelve nations that designate the continent to be used only for peaceful purposes. The treaty also excludes any nation from extending additional sovereign claims to Antarctica and bans nuclear explosions and dumping. Later, developing nations press for application of the common heritage principle to Antarctica.

1960   The United Nations Convention on the Law of the Sea meets for the second time (UNCLOS-II), but due to a stalemate between industrial marine powers and coastal nations, nothing is accomplished. The U.S. proposal to extend the territorial seas to 6 miles, in addition to a 6-mile fishing zone, is defeated by one vote.

The International Convention for the Safety of Life at Sea (SOLAS) is convened. This convention produces a major agreement regarding the safe operations of ships at sea to benefit crew and the shipping industry. The first version of the treaty was adopted in 1914 in response to the *Titanic* disaster in 1912 (see 1912). Attention to safety at sea is most important for those working on fishing boats and other mariners, whose jobs are often said to have some of the highest mortality rates in the world.

1962   Princeton geologist Harry Hess publishes *An Essay on Geopoetry,* which explains that the seafloor is always spreading due to magma from the earth's mantle welling up between rifts in the seafloor. The magma pushes the seafloor out, creating underwater mountains and valleys. It turns out this theory is only partially true. Oceans are born and die in cycles, like many other ecological functions. Currently, the Atlantic Ocean is expanding while the Pacific is shrinking, and estimates show that the Mediterranean Sea will shrink enough to bring Africa and Europe together at some time in the future (Borgese 1998).

1963   The Partial Test Ban Treaty is signed to ban nuclear testing in the ocean, atmosphere, or outer space.

1965   J. Tuzo Wilson proposes that continents drift and the seafloor expands because the earth's crust is made up of moving pieces, or plates. Wilson's explanation provides the mechanism that had been missing from Alfred Wegener's theory of continental drift, established fifty years earlier (see 1915).

The Soviet Union begins disposing of nuclear reactors into the Kara Sea. Seven of the sixteen reactors dumped still have fuel in them to this day. Radioactive wastes are also dumped into the Barents Sea around the same time by the Soviets. This practice goes unreported until 1993, when the Yablokov Report is released by the Russian government after the fall of the Soviet Union (Stokke 1998, 476).

1967   The Latin American Nuclear Weapon–Free Treaty bans nuclear weapons from 68 million square miles of Latin American waters (Westing 1992).

1969   The United States passes the National Environmental Policy Act, which becomes a model for many nations that are working to develop environmental policy in general. One of the main contributions of this act is to institute environmental impact statements as a way of determining policy. This particular tool is used in many nations all over the world.

The UN General Assembly proclaims that deep-seabed minerals on the high seas are the "common heritage of mankind," referencing an often-cited and impassioned speech by Arvid Pardoe (see chapter 5).

The International Whaling Commission institutes its first quota system to manage the number of whales killed each year. By this time, commercial whaling has been banned for gray, bowhead, right, humpback, and blue whales. Three years later, antiwhaling nations begin to call for a full moratorium on all commercial whaling (Andresen 1998, 442).

An oil field in California's Santa Barbara Channel ruptures on the seafloor (see chapter 5). The ensuing spill lasts for weeks, catalyzing environmental groups to oppose all oil drilling in the channel.

1971 The *Stella Maris* leaves port in Rotterdam amid protests. The ship's mission is to dump 650 tons of toxic waste into the North Sea. There are no regulations to stop the ship, and as a result of this incident, the 1972 Oslo Convention is called (see 1972).

The Soviet-U.S. Seabed Arms Control Treaty bans the placing of weapons of mass destruction on the ocean floor and in the subsea soil.

1972 The Soviet-U.S. Incidents at Sea Treaty is signed. This agreement establishes rules to avoid accidental military incidents at sea (Weeks 1992) (see chapter 5).

The Oslo Convention, or the Convention for the Prevention of Marine Pollution by Dumping from Ships and Aircraft, is signed largely as a result of protests surrounding the *Stella Maris* incident (see 1971). This agreement prohibits the dumping of toxic waste into the North Sea (Greene 1998).

The Stockholm Conference on the Human Environment adopts the ideal of sustainable development for the world environment. This conference is the first international effort to recognize limits on global resources, including the ocean (particularly regarding fisheries). The conference produces a resolution for a ten-year moratorium on commercial whaling, which the International Whaling Commission initially rejects. The IWC finally agrees to a moratorium in 1982, to be implemented in 1986.

The London Dumping Convention determines rules for the global dumping of toxic materials. The convention works on a three-tiered permit system of regulated, unregulated, and banned substances, and it is continually updated with new management schemes (such as making polluters pay for their actions and

1972
(cont.)

setting precautionary standards) and regulations on polluting at sea. Incinerating wastes and most nuclear waste dumping at sea are prohibited in this protocol.

1973

The International Convention for the Prevention of Pollution from Ships (MARPOL) is signed in November. However, the convention is so objectionable to the oil industry that it is amended in 1978 and does not go into force until 1983 (see chapter 2).

1974

The United Nations Convention on the Law of the Sea begins its third convention (UNCLOS-III). This final convention leads to a ten-year negotiation period and a ten-year ratification period. It is the most comprehensive legal tool for ocean management to date.

As a companion to the Oslo Convention (see 1972), the Paris Convention, or the Convention for the Prevention of Marine Pollution from Land-based Sources, is signed. Together, the two regimes make up what is called OSPAR, a larger regime to prevent North Sea pollution. The Paris Convention recognizes that a majority of pollution in the ocean starts inland and that to reduce ocean pollution, management must reduce inland sources of pollution.

The Convention on the Protection of the Marine Environment of the Baltic Sea Area (1974 Helsinki Convention) creates one of the first regional sea agreements to deal with Baltic Sea pollution. The discussions are driven by Nordic states, which have been mostly on the receiving end of this pollution. However, since the Baltic states, at this time, are a part of the Soviet bloc, the Helsinki Convention is primarily used to create a diplomatic space for research and communication. After the fall of the Soviet Union, the agreement becomes a means for establishing effective regional pollution control.

1975

The Australian government passes the Great Barrier Reef Marine Park Act, which designates the reef as a marine protected area. Later, the Great Barrier Reef also becomes a World Heritage Site (an internationally recognized area of importance).

The London Convention (see 1972) goes into effect, banning high-level nuclear waste from being dumped into the ocean. A further agreement to the convention (in 1993) will ban low- and medium-level nuclear waste as well. Russia continues to dump nuclear waste, however, under a technicality in the convention (Stokke 1998).

1977   The U.S. submersible *Alvin* discovers unique communities of organisms around deep-sea thermal vents formerly thought to be devoid of life. These organisms convert energy from the chemical and thermal riches of the vents instead of using solar radiation for photosynthesis.

U.S. president Jimmy Carter signs an agreement with Panama to give it control of the Panama Canal in the year 2000.

1978   The International Maritime Organization develops rules for treating and disposing sewage at sea, in addition to amending MARPOL (see 1973).

1979   The International Whaling Commission declares most of the Indian Ocean a sanctuary due to its widespread use by whales for calving. Sanctuaries generally are in effect for ten years. By consensus, the IWC has agreed to keep this area a sanctuary indefinitely (IWC 2001).

1982   The United Nations Convention on the Law of the Sea (UNCLOS-III) negotiations conclude, allowing nations to sign the treaty and then pursue ratification by their home governments.

The Paris Memorandum gives port states, or states that receive ships, partial responsibility for inspecting vessels in their harbor for compliance with safety and environmental requirements. This strategy is employed to reduce the flags of convenience problem (see chapter 2), but implementation of the memorandum has been sporadic and only marginally effective (Frankel 1995).

The International Whaling Commission votes to place a moratorium on all commercial whaling, starting in 1986.

1983   MARPOL 1973/1978 (see 1973 and chapter 2) goes into force.

1988   The environmental group Greenpeace begins a global boycott on seafood exported from Norway and Iceland because of the continued whaling practices of those nations. The boycott, most successful in Germany, costs Iceland U.S.$30 million, and a year later, whaling in that country completely ends.

The Committee for the Defense of the Flora and Fauna of the Gulf of Fonseca, a grassroots environmental group, is formed by disaffected fishers who had been edged out of ocean commons in Honduras by shrimp farmers. Shrimp farmers had fenced off common-ocean access areas and blocked local use for fishing. This effort reflects the growing movement of artisanal (or small-scale subsistence) fishers who must fight to maintain their access to resources. This particular organization will win global acclaim from larger environmental groups. It will also win the 1992 Global 500 Prize awarded by the United Nations and the seventeenth annual J. Paul Getty Prize awarded by the World Wildlife Fund for its conservation work in conjunction with local users (Stanley 1996).

The World Meteorological Organization, a UN agency that studies climate, appoints the Intergovernmental Panel on Climate Change (IPCC) (see chapter 8) to research global warming.

1989   The Basel Convention, or the International Convention on the Control of Transboundary Movements of Hazardous Wastes and Their Disposal, is adopted. One article of the convention prohibits exporting wastes to be dumped or incinerated at sea.

The *Exxon Valdez* oil tanker spill occurs off the coast of Alaska (see chapter 2).

1989–1991 The Cold War ends. This international breakthrough strengthens environmental agreements such as those regarding the Baltic Sea. Among other related effects, the United States withdraws some of its marine power from East Asia, which leads to a moderate arms race in the region by nations seeking to fill the gap.

1990   The U.S. Oil Pollution Act is passed into law as a result of the *Exxon Valdez* spill. The act, among other requirements, mandates all tankers in U.S. waters to have double hulls by the year 2010.

The first IPCC (see 1988 and chapter 8) report is issued. It warns that carbon dioxide levels will likely double in the next 100 years and the global average temperature will rise between 1.5 to 4.5°C (2.7 to 8.1°F) in the same period. The authors of the report believe this will result in rising sea levels, droughts, and floods and will threaten the security of food and water supplies. The report is important because it provides the scientific background to international negotiations for the Framework Convention on Climate Change, which will come out of the Rio Conference on Environment and Development in 1992.

1991   The IWC's revised management procedure is brought to the general members by the Science Commission of the International Whaling Commission. This procedure uses a wildlife management scheme to reintroduce commercial whaling. The procedure is later approved by the IWC, but it is still not implemented as of the writing of this book (Andresen 1998, 444) (see chapter 2).

1992   The United Nations Conference on Environment and Development convenes in Rio de Janeiro to reaffirm the work of the Stockholm Conference, as well as to produce a plan for global conservation through its Agenda 21 (see 1972 and chapter 5). Among the groundbreaking agreements made at this "Earth Summit" are the Convention on Biological Diversity and the Framework Convention on Climate Change (see 1990). The climate agreement is signed by 154 nations and sets 1990 as the benchmark year for emissions reforms.

1992
(cont.)

MARPOL (see 1973) requires all tankers to have double hulls by 2015. This requirement is largely a result of lessons learned from the *Exxon Valdez* spill.

The Kazakh Parliament condemns the Aral Sea basin as an "ecological disaster zone." The Aral Sea, which is a salt lake or an inland sea, was at one time the world's fourth-largest inland body of water. However, as a result of Soviet river diversions for agricultural use, it has begun to dry up. In fact, the Aral Sea has lost so much water that it is now two bodies—the Little Aral Sea and the Large Aral Sea—because it is dissected by a land bridge (Smith 1995).

Iceland formally withdraws from the International Whaling Commission after the IWC denies an interim plan to resume commercial whaling of specific species, even though Iceland has not hunted whales since 1989.

The North Atlantic Marine Mammals Commission (NAMMCO) is established to provide an alternative to the International Whaling Commission. NAMMCO favors commercial whaling.

1994

The United Nations Convention on the Law of the Sea (UNCLOS-III) goes into effect, completing a process that took nearly forty years.

The International Whaling Commission creates the Southern Ocean Sanctuary in Antarctica. Twenty-three nations vote for the sanctuary, with only Japan opposing it. Japan has been reported by Greenpeace to have purposefully whaled within the sanctuary. Australia continues to advocate for a global marine sanctuary that would include all waters.

The Alliance of Small Island States demands more dramatic emission reductions than is agreed to in the Framework Convention on Climate Change (see 1992). Also in this year, the climate change accord goes into force; by the time it is effective, 186 countries are party to the agreement. (There are about 189 countries in the world.)

1995   On March 9, a Canadian coast guard boat fires shots across the bow of the Spanish trawler *Estai* before confiscating the vessel for fishing turbot, a straddling species. This begins the turbot war between Spain and Canada (see chapter 3).

1997   The Kyoto Protocol of the Framework Convention on Climate Change (see 1992) is signed. The importance of the Kyoto Protocol is that it commits industrialized nations to an average 5.4 percent cut in emissions of greenhouse gases such as carbon dioxide (produced by most engines) from their 1990 levels. The United States refuses to ratify this agreement.

1998   The Galapagos Marine Preserve is created to protect the waters around the Galapagos Islands and the Galapagos National Park (1959), which encompasses most of these islands belonging to Ecuador.

The UN Year of the Oceans is declared as a way for the international community to focus attention on ocean governance.

2000   The scientific community reassesses global-warming predictions. The forecast maximum over the next hundred years is raised from 4.5 to 6°C (8.1 to 10.8°F).

U.S. president Bill Clinton creates the largest U.S. nature preserve in an area around northwestern Hawaii. The preserve is 84 million acres in size and is designed to protect coral reefs and wildlife habitats in the area. Seventy percent of the nation's reefs exist in this area.

The European Scientific Committee for Food, which is concerned with food safety, warns that dioxins and other industry-made chemicals proliferate in European regional seas, such as the North Sea, to the extent that fish from the area should not be eaten on a frequent basis.

2000 (cont.)	Paleontologists from the University of Arizona report that dams affect ocean life. Their studies show that the dams on the Colorado River cut off the nutrients and river flow that previously fed marine life, such as clams at the mouth of the river and in the ocean. Clams in that area, which normally numbered 6 billion, are now relatively rare (Muro 2001).
2001	On December 11, the United Nations Conference on Straddling Fish Stocks and Highly Migratory Fish Stocks goes into force. This agreement is a separate part of the Law of the Sea Treaty, which sets tangible conservation limits on fish stocks that cross international and high-seas boundaries (see chapter 2).
2002	From August 26 to September 4, global leaders meet at Johannesburg, South Africa, at the World Summit on Sustainable Development. They agree to promote more transparency (making information available to the public and press) regarding coastal management and fisheries and promise to return world fish stocks to their maximum levels by 2015. However, divisions between rich and poor countries keep the leaders from making any dramatic changes in the way conservation measures are carried out on the World Ocean.

On November 13, a storm cracks the single hull of the oil tanker *Prestige* off the coast of Spain. The tanker, loaded with 70,000 tons of oil, is refused port by Spain and consequently sinks 130 miles off the coast. Spanish coastal fishers rush to harvest what they can while hundred of miles of seashore are coated with oil. Policy requiring double-hull ships is already approved for 2020 worldwide and for 2015 in the United States and the European Union, but critics say this is too long to wait. Single-hull tankers are involved in 70 percent of such disasters, and experts agree a double hull would probably have prevented the *Prestige* spill.

References

Andresen, Steinar. 1998. "The Making and Implementation of Whaling Policies." In D. Victor, K. Raustiala, and Eugene Skolnikoff, eds., *The Implementation and Effectiveness of International Environmental Commitments*. Cambridge, MA: MIT Press.

Becher, Anne. 1998. *Biodiversity: A Reference Handbook*. Santa Barbara, CA: ABC-CLIO.

Borgese, Elisabeth Mann. 1998. *The Oceanic Circle: Governing the Seas as a Global Resource*. New York: United Nations University Press.

Deacon, Margaret. 1997. *Scientists and the Sea, 1650–1900: A Study of Marine Science*. Brookefield, VT: Ashgate Publishing.

Dimitrov, George. 1992. In J. Goldblatt, ed., *Maritime Security: The Building of Confidence*. New York: United Nations Press.

Electric Library. 2000. "Sextant." In *Encyclopedia.com*. Available online at http://encyclopedia.com. Accessed on November 15, 2002.

Erikson, Erik. 1969. *Gandhi's Truth: On the Origins of Militant Nonviolence*. New York: W. W. Norton.

Frankel, Ernst. 1995. *Ocean Environmental Management: A Primer on the Role of Oceans and How to Maintain Their Contributions to Life on Earth*. Englewood Cliffs, NJ: Prentice-Hall.

Glassner, Martin Ira. 1990. *Neptune's Domain: A Political Geography of the Sea*. Boston: Unwin Hyman.

Greene, Owen. 1998. "Implementation Review and the Baltic Sea Regime." In D. Victor, K. Raustiala, and Eugene Skolnikoff, eds., *The Implementation and Effectiveness of International Environmental Commitments*. Cambridge, MA: MIT Press.

International Maritime Organization (IMO). 2001. "International Convention for the Safety of Life at Sea (SOLAS), 1974." Available online at http://www.imo.org. Accessed on November 15, 2002.

International Whaling Commission (IWC). 2001. "Catch Limits, Etc." Available online at http://ourworld.compuserve.com/homepages/iwcoffice/Catches.htm#Sanctuaries. Accessed on November 15, 2002.

Muro, Mark. 2001. "Silence of the Clams." In *High Country News*, February 12.

Prager, Ellen J., with Sylvia Earle. 2000. *The Oceans*. New York. McGraw-Hill.

Smith, David R. 1995. "Kazakhstan." In Phillip Pryde, ed., *Environmental Resources and Constraints in the Former Soviet Republics*. Boulder, CO: Westview Press.

Stanley, Denise. 1996. "David vs. Goliath: Fishermen Conflicts with Mariculturists in Honduras." In H. Collinson, ed., *Green Guerrillas: Environmental Conflicts and Initiatives in Latin America and the Caribbean.* New York: Monthly Review Press for the Latin America Bureau.

Stokke, Olav Schram. 1998. "Nuclear Dumping in Arctic Seas." In D. Victor, K. Raustiala, and Eugene Skolnikoff, eds., *The Implementation and Effectiveness of International Environmental Commitments.* Cambridge, MA: MIT Press.

Weeks, Stanley. 1992. "Measures to Prevent Major Incidents at Sea." In J. Goldblatt, ed., *Maritime Security: The Building of Confidence.* New York: United Nations Press.

Westing, Arthur. 1992. "Environmental Dimensions of Maritime Security." In J. Goldblatt, ed., *Maritime Security: The Building of Confidence.* New York: United Nations Press.

5

People and Events

This chapter provides profiles of a set of people and events that have made their mark on ocean governance and policy. The events in this chapter were chosen because they represent milestones in history that have helped frame ocean management as it develops over time. The Grand Banks fishery closing, for example, is an event that places the importance of good fishery management in context by showing what happens when fishery management fails. In this way, the Grand Banks event is important for the evolution of ocean management, and policymakers will continue to refer back to this failure for some time.

Similarly, the people in this chapter have been chosen for their contributions either to ocean science or to political (including diplomatic) ideas about the ocean; this set of knowledge and ideas forms the basis on which ocean management operates. Together, the works of the scientific and political figures presented here demonstrate that oceans are used and governed through a combination of knowledge and aspirations. Science provides knowledge about the physical oceanic universe, whereas politics mediates the desires surrounding the World Ocean, which may or may not be products of scientific knowledge. Both approaches inform one another in ocean management. For example, when the crew of the *Challenger* (see entry) discovered valuable metallic spheres at the bottom of the ocean, a desire to harvest them was created. Politics continues to mediate this specific desire between private or global ownership and mining of the spheres. The latter involves the common heritage argument detailed in chapter 2.

Elisabeth Mann Borgese (1918–2002)

Until her death in February 2002, Elisabeth Mann Borgese was one of the greatest proponents of the common heritage idea as well as the effort to use the ocean for peaceful purposes (see chapter 3). She was a professor of political science at Dalhousie University in Canada. Her work consistently focused on ways to use the ocean to decrease worldwide financial inequality, as well as the importance of protecting the marine ecosystems and resources. Borgese had worked directly with Arvid Pardoe (see entry) in advocating the common heritage idea as the central principle of modern ocean management. By calling on this idea, Borgese and Pardoe essentially challenged the focus of world politics that usually sees nations as the most important actors. To Borgese, the state was important, but her work suggests that people, regardless of divisions between states, were more important still.

She founded and organized the *Pacem in Maribus* ("Peace in the Oceans") conferences that annually focus on global governance and peaceful uses of the seas—uses that do not harm people or ecosystems. Violent uses of the ocean would include the testing of nuclear bombs on islands or in the water. Borgese also founded and chaired the International Ocean Institute, which conducts independent research and advocates for peaceful uses of the oceans and the uplift of developing nations. For Borgese, the oceans connected people to nature and to each other; but for this connection to occur, uses of the ocean had to be nonviolent and nondestructive. She furthered such ideas during her tenure as an adviser to the United Nations Environment Programme, the United Nations Educational, Scientific and Cultural Organization, and the World Bank.

Borgese was highly decorated for her work. She won the United Nations Sasakawa Environment Prize, the Francis Assisi Environment Prize, and the Order of Canada for her efforts to fundamentally change the unsustainable governance of the oceans. Her publications include various editions of *The Ocean Yearbook* (which she co-edited), *The Oceanic Circle: Governing the Seas as a Global Resource,* and several UN pamphlets on the ocean.

Robert Boyle (1627–1691)

Boyle was a pioneering British scientist who is credited with several important discoveries related to the ocean. Born in Ireland, he is known as a founder of modern chemistry and was one of the first scientists to systematically publish his findings. He is also credited with the invention of a practical vacuum pump, with which he proved that air was necessary for both flame and sound. Due to these and other contributions, his place in British scientific history has been compared to that of Isaac Newton.

He is perhaps most famous for Boyle's Law, which states that when temperature is constant, the volume of a particular body of gas is inversely proportionate to the pressure exerted on that gas. Simply stated, as gas comes under pressure, its volume reduces; conversely, gas expands with less pressure. Among other things, this law helps predict weather changes through the use of a barometer, an instrument that measures the changes in air pressure that indicate upcoming fronts and other weather patterns.

However, Boyle's most important contribution for ocean management is found in the four books he authored in the 1660s and 1670s, which represented the most comprehensive understanding of oceanography at the time. Prior to that point, it was assumed that the sea was salty only at the top. Further, it was assumed that the less salty depths were warmer, since the earth's core contained known "fires" (now understood to be molten rock). Boyle's research, however, proved that salt was present all over the ocean and at all depths. Also, he said that different depths of the ocean had distinct characteristics. One characteristic was that the ocean generally became colder as depth increased (Deacon 1997).

In addition, Boyle was the first person to make a distinction between acids, bases, and salts. Indeed, his contributions in regard to salts and ocean temperatures paved the way for the contemporary understanding of currents. Currents move warmer and colder water through a global "conveyor belt," which is essential to the regulation of the earth's temperature. These currents are divided into colder, more saline waters at the bottom of the ocean that move toward the equator and warmer, less saline waters at the upper levels of the ocean that move toward the poles. The functioning of the conveyor belt is complicated by winds and the spin of the earth, but in general, different water temperatures move around the globe as a function of temperature and density (the more salt, the more dense the water). Currents are now understood to keep the temperatures of land areas more stable. Moreover, an understanding of the currents has been vital to navigation throughout history.

Boyle was also a founding member of the London Royal Society, which is currently the oldest scientific organization in existence. His publications include *The Sceptical Chemist* (1661), *Origin of Forms and Qualities According to the Corpuscular Philosophy* (1666), and *Discourse of Things above Reason* (1681).

Rachel Carson (1907–1964)

Rachel Carson, an American marine biologist, is often described as one of the most influential people in the modern environmental movement. She is most famous for her book *Silent Spring*, which was published in 1962 and documented the horrors wrought by pollution on the living world. Her writing stressed the interrelationships of living things and argued that food supplies should be free of poisons (namely, pesticides).

Carson's first three books focused on the ocean. *The Sea around Us*, published in 1951, won the coveted National Book Award and sold over a million copies. *The Sea around Us* and *Silent Spring* continue to be important contributions to marine literature. Carson's writing is said to have moved a generation into environmental action, and former vice-president Al Gore credited her for inspiring and generating the demand for the U.S. Environmental Protection Agency. Also, she is largely credited with having DDT, a pesticide, banned in the United States.

Carson was born in Springdale, Pennsylvania, and educated at Pennsylvania College for Women. She received her master's in biology at Johns Hopkins University, and for a time, she taught zoology at the University of Maryland. She then accepted a position as an aquatic biologist at the U.S. Bureau of Fisheries and later the Fish and Wildlife Service. She held this latter position from 1936 to 1952. After the success of *The Sea around Us*, she was able to retire. Ten years later, she published *Silent Spring*. Rachel Carson died of cancer in 1964.

HMS *Challenger* (1873–1876)

Until the late nineteenth century, knowledge of the ocean was limited to reports of seafarers and the regional work of scientists. The voyage of the British research vessel *Challenger*, a 200-foot steamer, changed this trend, since it was the first global voyage exclusively dedicated to a scientific purpose. The crew's official mission was to find out all they could about the world's oceans. After the *Challenger*, scientific institutes such as Woods Hole and the Scripps Institution have continued to regularly send ships out to sea exclusively to further human understanding of the ocean.

The information logged by the *Challenger* crew demonstrated to the scientific community that science-based voyages could have rich results. *The Report of the Scientific Results of the Exploring Voyage of H.M.S.* Challenger *During the Years 1873–76* took about ten years to compile even with the help of over a hundred scientists examining the specimens collected. This report takes up fifty very large volumes. Even today, the *Challenger* report provides a bedrock of ocean concepts that are still used by contemporary oceanographers.

Under the scientific guidance of Wyville Thomson (1830–1882), the *Challenger* succeeded in circumnavigating the entire globe and logging over 70,000 nautical miles in under three and a half years. To complete this task, a crew of 240 people was employed. As the ship went around the world, it made hundreds of stops to sample waters and measure depths. The crew also lowered nets into the water to catch whatever they could at a chosen depth. Using this dredging process, the ship's crew measured depths of 26,000 feet (936 meters) and recorded more than 4,000 new species. Among the more important findings for ocean management was that life did indeed exist at the greatest depths of the ocean. Knowing that the ocean depths are not "dead" gives ocean managers another reason to curb ocean dumping.

As noted in the introduction to this chapter, the *Challenger* crew also discovered the existence of valuable metal spheres at the bottom of the ocean. However, it was not until a hundred years later, during the Law of the Sea negotiations, that these metallic nodules were thought of as a commercially and technically feasible mining opportunity.

For all these reasons, the activities of the *Challenger* are often considered among the most important early milestones in modern oceanography and ocean management. Manganese nodules, however, are still not mined on a commercial scale due to the high costs of collecting them from the deep ocean floors.

Jacques-Yves Cousteau (1910–1997)

Jacques Cousteau was born in St. André de Cubzac, France, in 1910. He is well known for creating, with Emile Gagnon, the first self-contained underwater breathing apparatus (SCUBA) in 1943. Prior to this invention, divers had to work in bulky suits that were attached to a boat on the water's surface by a line of oxygen.

SCUBA equipment gave divers the freedom to swim underwater without this confinement and allowed them to see and experience parts of the ocean that were unknown to that point. Cousteau also designed a submersible vessel for scientific research and filming and a camera housing that could be used underwater (Cousteau Society 2001).

Captain Cousteau was honored throughout the world and held prized positions in marine science and conservation. He advised the United Nations and the World Bank to help them develop the oceans in a sustainable manner. Also, Cousteau was one of the few foreign members of the U.S. National Academy of Sciences and served as director of the Musée Océanographique of Monaco for thirty-one years. He co-authored more than fifty books and produced more than a hundred films. In addition, he was responsible for a very popular television series, *The Undersea World of Jacques Cousteau*, that was produced from 1968 to 1976. During that period, he worked on his ship, the *Calypso*, traveling around the world to document marine ecosystems.

Cousteau was a staunch advocate for ocean conservation, and in 1973, he founded the Cousteau Society, an environmental nonprofit organization that fights for marine preservation (see chapter 8). This society is still an important player in international ocean management and policy.

Sylvia Earle (1935–)

Sylvia Earle, whose work encompasses science, government, and exploration, is one of today's most prominent marine biologists. With over 6,000 hours of underwater diving and research experience, she is a world leader in terms of her knowledge of the undersea world.

Earle was the first woman to serve as the chief scientist of the National Oceanic and Atmospheric Administration (in the early 1990s), and she also holds the world record for diving. In 1979, she walked on the bottom of the ocean floor off the shores of Oahu at a depth of 1,250 feet. That was and still is the deepest a human being has ever gone under the ocean without being in a submarine. In recognition of this feat, Earle was dubbed "Her Deepness" by the *New Yorker* and the *New York Times*.

Earle first became renowned in her field for the extensive cataloging of plants from the Gulf of Mexico in her celebrated doctoral dissertation. However, she became well known to the general public after leading the Tektite II mission off the coast of the Bahamas. Tektite was a program sponsored by the Department of the Interior, the U.S. Navy, and the National Aeronautics and Space Administration (NASA); it sent oceanographers to live 50 feet underwater for several weeks for direct ocean learning. She had applied to be a part of Tektite I and indeed had more research hours underwater than any other candidate, but the program leaders disapproved of sending men and women together into the ocean for an extended time. During the two-week mission in 1970, the four women involved were the focus of so much media attention that they received a ticker-tape parade to the White House after they emerged from the water (American Academy of Achievement 2001).

This newfound popularity led Sylvia Earle to a life of public speaking and advocacy for marine research and pollution prevention. She also wrote for *National Geographic* and began to produce films and books, such as *Sea Change: A Message of the Oceans*, published in 1995. Today, Earle is an explorer-in-residence for the National Geographic Society and is director of the society's Sustainable Seas Expedition.

Grand Banks Fishery Closing (1992)

The governments of Newfoundland and Labrador in Canada closed their northern cod fishery in 1992 because the species population had collapsed as a result of overfishing. By 1995, all cod and flounder fisheries were closed, and strict catch limits were imposed for turbot and ocean perch.

Northern cod is a groundfish (a fish that feeds on the ocean floor) that is very specific to the Grand Banks area. The area's rich fishery was the basis for settlement in northeastern Canada. However, between 1988 and 1993, the cod catch dropped by 90 percent. Since each 1,000 pounds of fish provides about thirty full-time jobs, the fish were not the only casualties of the fallen fishery. Canadian workers, particularly in Newfoundland, lost about 35,000 jobs. Several plants that processed the cod also closed. The Newfoundland fishing industry, which depended on groundfish for 94 percent of its economy, remains in financial crisis even today. Small fishers who owned their boats had investments that became nearly worthless during a moratorium, and even large corporations have had to shut down their Newfoundland operations. The Canadian government has since instituted programs to transfer the fishing industry workers into other careers, despite the fact that many generations have dedicated their lives to the outdoor work.

The Grand Banks are a series of submarine plateaus off the island of Newfoundland. Because the sea depth there is raised, warm currents pass over the area, creating a region of abundant sea life. Previously, cod had been so plentiful in the Grand Banks that mariners are said to have simply lowered their buckets into the water to catch them.

Although the fishery was used as early as the 1400s by Portuguese and Basque fishers, it was not until John Cabot passed through on his way to the New World in 1497 that the Grand Banks became well known. Thereafter, the area was intensively fished by England, France, Portugal, and Spain. Later, Canada and the United States would also heavily exploit the area (Governments of Newfoundland and Labrador 2001).

The fishery collapsed so dramatically that after the moratorium on groundfish was put in place, cod populations continued to decline. Under the moratorium for nearly a decade as of this writing, the fishery has still not significantly recovered, and the prospects for it reopening any time soon remain dim (Government of Canada 1996). The Grand Banks fishery collapse is a good example of how people can be directly affected by a failure of ocean management.

Hugo Grotius (1583–1645)

Hugo Grotius is most famous in ocean management for popularizing the term *freedom of the seas* through his treatise *Mare Liberum* (see chapter 1). He is also recognized as one of the chief advocates for "natural law," or law that applies to everyone and is anchored in religion, morality, and simple reason. Grotius's work on natural law strongly influenced philosophers such as Thomas Hobbes, who used it to help justify modern social theory. Natural law is probably one reason why Grotius applied his mare liberum doctrine to all nations.

Grotius was hired by the Dutch East India Company to argue on its behalf for access to trade routes controlled by the Portuguese. The Dutch were at war with Spain and were also in tension with Portugal. Spain and Portugal had laid claims to vast areas of the ocean, and they were attempting to exclude others from that territory, among them the very strong Dutch who eventually muscled their way into the waters by taking a Portuguese vessel. Grotius was hired to defend this action under the principle that all nations had an equal right to sea-lanes of transportation and the riches beneath them (Grotius 1972).

Grotius was famous in his own time and was even called the "miracle of Holland" due to his extraordinary life and achievements. He began studying at the university in Leiden, the Netherlands, at the age of eleven. There, he studied math, physics, Hebrew, and Arabic. At age fifteen, he was part of the Dutch embassy to France. While in France, he completed his doctorate in law at the Université d'Orléans. He started a promising law career and became the Netherlands historian at age twenty-one. Three years later, Grotius accepted a position as the advocate-fiscal of Holland (a post much like attorney general). In the year following his appointment, he wrote the *Law of Prize*, which continues to influence international thought and which contained a chapter entitled *"Mare Liberum."* When this book was finally published in the nineteenth century, it was discovered that *Mare Liberum*, released as a separate essay in 1608 or 1609, was not an anonymous work as previously thought.

In the mid-1630s, Grotius became embroiled in a debate about Calvinism. He eventually found himself on the losing side and spent two years in jail. While imprisoned, he continued to read and write scholarly works. His wife, Maria, is said to have helped him in a daring escape in a trunk thought to be filled with books. After this episode, Grotius would never be able to be a permanent resident of the Netherlands again; he would spend the rest of his life as an ambassador of Sweden to France. He died of exhaustion after being in a shipwreck in the Baltic. At the end of his life, he declared, "By understanding many things, I have accomplished nothing" (Uzgalis 1999).

Johan Hjort (1869–?)

Johan Hjort, a Norwegian zoologist, changed the way fishery studies were conducted as a result of his work in the early twentieth century. He received his Ph.D. at the Zoological Station in Naples, Italy, and returned to Oslo in the 1890s. He is known for two major achievements in fishery science. First, he divided fisheries up by the year each fish in a species was born, which he called a "year-class." He was able to date fish by looking at rings and bands on their bones and scales. After separating a batch of fish into their proper year-classes, he could determine fluctuations in fish populations over several years.

After working for some time on herring populations, he realized that in certain years, there were bountiful and strong populations whereas other year-classes were much less populous. After determining that these fluctuations were not caused by fishers, he looked to environmental causes. His findings revealed that during years when there was a great amount of plankton in the herring fisheries, those particular year-classes became strong and plentiful, since less of the population died from malnutrition. (Strong year-classes of herring can live twenty years or longer.) Large sections of a year-class, he discovered, died off when there was not enough plankton to feed them. (Plankton is the range of plants and animals that drift passively in the sea.) For ocean management, this meant that protecting fish required protecting plankton.

Incidents at Sea Treaty Signing (1972)

In May 1972, the United States and the Soviet Union signed an agreement to avoid accidental warfare at sea. The full name of this treaty is the Agreement between the Government of the United States of America and the Government of the Union of Soviet Socialist Republics on the Prevention of Incidents on and over the High Seas; it is commonly known as the Incidents at Sea Treaty (INCSEA).

At the time of the treaty, the Cold War was on, and the Soviet Union and the United States had two of the strongest navies in the world. The United States, through its allies Japan and South Korea, had established a continued presence in the Pacific. The Soviet Union did not have a similar "forward projection," or forces present across the world, but it did have a policy of being wherever the U.S. Navy was on the high seas in order to keep the pressure on its antagonist. In the background of the Cold War was the continued threat posed by nuclear weapons, and any overt act of war by one superpower against the other had potentially global and genocidal effects. With tensions high, the superpowers agreed that an accidental war should be prevented.

INCSEA's main purpose was to establish confidence and security with regard to military forces at sea with the exception of submarines, which are suspiciously exempt from the treaty even though a submarine mishap could also have started an accidental war. Under INCSEA, the two antagonistic navies were banned from making threatening maneuvers unless they actually intended to commit an act of war. Such things as pointing guns at another ship, running mock ramming attacks, and employing attack-oriented surveillance were prohibited. The agreement also allowed for the two countries to exchange military visits and conduct talks, and it required advance notice for large-scale maneuvers. It also kept the two navies at safe distances to avoid collisions.

Prior to the agreement, there were at least 100 U.S.-Soviet incidents at sea, which included collisions, near misses, shots fired across bows, and other aggravated events (Lynn-Jones 1993). INCSEA successfully reduced the tensions between the superpowers and subsequently inspired similar agreements between Soviet and European navies, as well as many regional agreements around the world. Now that the Soviet Union has been dissolved and replaced by the Commonwealth of Independent States and the Russian Federation, INSCEA serves as a bridge between these diverse governments. Military officials regularly visit other countries, transparent navy budgets are more available, and the seas are more peaceful for international military forces than they have been for a long time.

Tommy Thong Bee Koh (1937–)

Ambassador Tommy Thong Bee Koh is best known as the president of the third United Nations Convention on the Law of the Sea, which ran from 1980 to 1982. He is widely acknowledged for aiding stalemates throughout his tenure during critical moments of impasse in order to keep the Law of the Sea and the common heritage notion alive.

Koh received graduate degrees in law and criminology from Harvard and Cambridge, respectively, with honorary degrees and awards from Yale, Columbia, Stanford, and Georgetown Universities. He has received several awards from different countries and organizations, such as the 1996 Elizabeth Haub Prize from the University of Brussels and the International Council on Environmental Law. Most of these awards reflect Koh's public service on the international level for both the United Nations and the World Trade Organization, where he has helped to settle disputes and encourage ecologically pragmatic diplomacy.

Koh first worked internationally as a permanent ambassador of Singapore. Currently, he is the director of the Institute of Policy Studies in Singapore, while still holding an "at-large" ambassadorship for the island nation. Ten years after his presidency of the Law of the Sea convention, he took on another role at the United Nations Conference on Environment and Development (see entry) in Rio de Janeiro, Brazil, in 1992. At this "Earth Summit," he presided over the negotiations for Agenda 21, perhaps the most important outcome of the conference.

Miriam Levering (1917–1991)

Miriam Levering was the heart of an important nongovernmental organization, the Neptune Group. This organization existed solely to aid the development and success of the third Law of the Sea Treaty by continually pressing for U.S. leadership and involvement in the agreement. The Neptune Group was credited by Tommy Koh (see entry) as one of the groups that was instrumental in keeping the difficult and tenuous negotiations of the last convention, which lasted about a decade, viable. Neptune's members accomplished this by making three contributions: they provided delegates to the convention, independent scientific experts who could be called on to answer specialized questions; they provided aid to the negotiators of developing nations; and they provided an informal setting where delegates could talk more freely and negotiate more comfortably. (Such settings often prove more productive than formal meetings.)

Levering's husband, Sam, was the head of the U.S. Committee for the Oceans, a lobbying group founded in 1972. The couple met at Cornell, and they were both leaders in the "international federalist" movement, which sought a strong role for the United Nations in order to curb war. Both were also active in various peace movements and were associated with the Quakers and other religious groups working to stem international violence. Sam Levering was asked to work with and head the Committee for the Oceans, with a mandate to increase a rule of law for nations that would presumably help to delegate more influence to a global governing body.

Work for the Neptune Group started when the Nixon administration, through the efforts of Louis Sohn of Harvard University, published a draft law of the sea proposal in 1970. Under this draft, the United States proposed that revenues from mineral leases beyond the 200-mile boundaries of coastal nations should be shared to aid developing nations. Through the American Mining Congress lobbying group, mining interests immediately pushed for bills in the U.S. Congress to unilaterally oppose this common heritage implementation.

Miriam Levering was a fund-raiser and created important relationships that allowed the Neptune Group to enjoy occasional successes against larger and better-funded organizations opposed to the common heritage idea. Neptune is a name ascribed by Law of the Sea delegates to Miriam and Sam Levering and a group of other core peace advocates who continually opposed the lobbying efforts of the U.S. mining industry to block the common heritage concept. It is hard to measure the success of this group, since the negotiations for the final Convention of the Law of the Sea were meant to last only two to three years and the final ratification of the United States has not yet occurred. But it is possible that the group's efforts made the treaty negotiable until the last minute when the Reagan administration, two weeks prior to the end of the meeting in 1982, announced that the United States would not participate further. Of course, most of the other countries in the world did sign and ratify the Law of the Sea, which may have been partially a result of the individual effort provided by Miriam Levering and others within the Neptune Group.

HMS *Lusitania* (1915)

On May 1, 1915, the *Lusitania* left for its two hundred and second trip across the Atlantic, departing from New York and heading for England. Great Britain had gone to war with Germany less than a year prior, and World War I was in full swing. Germany had declared the oceans fair game for acts of war and routinely sent submarines to the Atlantic to sink as many Allied vessels as possible. British officials knew that the *Lusitania* was taking a risk by traveling through submarine-infested waters, and some historians suggest that they sent the ship through more slowly than normal to make it a target and thereby draw the United States into the war. The German U-boat that eventually sank the *Lusitania* had already sunk two ships one day earlier, but British officials did not warn the *Lusitania* crew. Also, warnings posted in the newspaper by the German Embassy to passengers in the United States had been ignored.

On May 7, the *Lusitania* crossed paths with a German U-20 submarine on a mission to sink British vessels. The U-boat sank the ocean liner with two torpedoes and left the area as hundreds scrambled for lifeboats, but most of the passengers drowned. In all, 1,190 people died, over 100 of whom were U.S. citizens. The Germans accused the United States of loading the *Lusitania* with arms for Britain to use against them, which was true, though there were no soldiers on board. Pressure mounted for the United States to enter the war, but President Woodrow Wilson would not bow to this pressure until several U.S. ships were sunk by Germany in 1917.

The ships sunk in 1917 present a lesson in realpolitik, or politics about the sheer strength and militancy of a nation. Citing the idea of the freedom of the seas, the United States claimed it had a right to use the Atlantic waters without having its ships molested by German attacks. Germany saw the trips between the United States and Britain as threats, as the two countries were no doubt secretly working together. Thus, Germany warned that it would sink all the ships it possibly could that appeared to threaten its national security. When Berlin followed through with this threat, the United States was put into the position of either backing down and looking as if it had lost power to Germany or going to war to keep what it thought was the right of free passage. Thus, the United States saw itself quite literally in the middle of "gunboat diplomacy," or international relations that rely on force and threats of force. Many other factors played a role in the U.S. entry into World War I, but these conceptions of power also were important. The *Lusitania* incident is viewed by some historians as the beginning of the struggle between the United States and Germany.

Matthew Fontaine Maury (1806–1873)

Matthew Fontaine Maury was a midshipman of the U.S. Navy, though he later fought as a commander in the Confederate Navy during the American Civil War. He is often described as the father of oceanography as a result of writing the textbook *Physical Geography of the Sea*, published in 1855. The work of other early oceanographers such as Edward Forbes, just prior to Maury, and even ancient scientists of the ocean, among them Aristotle (see chapter 4) should not be overlooked. Nonetheless, Maury made several important and preliminary contributions to the study of the oceans, both as a scientist and as a naval officer.

Maury spent a significant amount of time on the ocean as a sailor. In fact, during his second tour of duty with the navy, he was aboard the *Vincennes* when it became the first U.S. warship to circumnavigate the globe. This gave Maury practical experience and knowledge of the oceans and how to traverse them, and it was in the arena of navigation and naval operations that he would make his most important mark.

As the first superintendent of the U.S. Naval Observatory (previously the Depot of Charts and Instruments), he became well known for his navigational expertise. Due to his ability to chart a course through the most efficient routes on the ocean, he could sometimes reduce the length of a trip by a week's time. During his tenure at the observatory, he advocated for the establishment of an educational institution for sailors, and in 1845, the U.S. Naval Academy in Annapolis, Maryland, was founded. Also while in this post, he was made the U.S. representative to the International Congress (an international meeting) at Brussels. At this 1853 conference, he requested that oceanographic data, such as information on currents and winds, be recorded on all naval and merchant marine ships. His process of documenting oceanographic data was soon adopted internationally and is still a vital source for oceanographers.

During this period in U.S. history, tension was building between the North and South, and a few days after Virginia declared its independence from the United States, Maury became a naval officer for the Confederate Navy. While serving the Confederates, he continued working on naval advances, and he became the first American to successfully detonate an underwater bomb with electricity. After the Civil War ended, Maury took his ship to England, where he stayed for some time before returning under the threat of being arrested for treason as a consequence of his work with the rebels. This threat was annulled when President Andrew Johnson boarded his ship as it neared the U.S. shore and offered him amnesty. Thereafter, he was a professor at the Virginia Military Institute, until his death in 1873 (Hodge 2002).

More information on the life or work of Maury is available in his text *The Physical Geography of the Sea* and his letters, which are offered online by the Virginia Military Institute at http://www.vmi.edu/archives/manuscripts/maury/mfmpaprs.html.

Minimata Disaster (1932–1968)

From 1932 until 1968, the Chisso Corporation, a plastics manufacturer, dumped about 27 tons of mercury compounds into the Minimata Bay in Japan. Japanese citizens suffered diseases and death as a result of the poisoning that ensued, and even as late as 1993, they had not fully been compensated by the corporation.

After Chisso had been polluting Minimata Bay for twenty years, the citizens of the area began coming down with strange nervous system symptoms, and at the same time, people noticed cats "committing suicide" and birds dropping to the ground. In the mid-1950s, a physician named Hajime Hosokawa linked the nervous system disorders to his patients' fish diets; this led him to investigate the sea and the pollution caused by the Chisso Corporation. In an effort to divert attention from the situation, Chisso stopped dumping in the ocean and began dumping in a Japanese river instead, with the result that nearby residents also became sick. Research commissions backed by the corporation argued that the poisoning came from natural occurrences of mercury, but Hosokawa kept doing tests to pin the responsibility on Chisso. At the same time, the corporation gathered signatures from citizens waiving Chisso's responsibility.

About three thousand victims suffered from "Minimata disease," and many never received any compensation. It was not until the use of mercury in the corporation's production process became obsolete that the Chisso actually stopped dumping mercury compounds into Japanese water (Littlefield 1997).

Fridtjof Nansen (1861–1930)

Fridtjof Nansen was a Norwegian Nobel Prize winner, Arctic explorer, scientist, and international diplomat. As a result of his North Pole expedition, he discovered that a deep Arctic Ocean surrounded the Pole and that there was a strong transpolar current. He was also one of the founding fathers of the International Council for the Exploration of the Sea (ICES) in 1902 (see chapter 8). Although his expedition did not reach the Pole, he had explored farther north than anyone else at the time, and on returning, he was met with international fame. Today, his life's work is continued at the Fridtjof Nansen Institute near Oslo (see chapter 8), a leading intellectual hub for ocean policy.

He became a professor of zoology and oceanography at the university in what is now Oslo. In 1905, he was made a Norwegian ambassador to Great Britain during the effort to separate Norway from Sweden.

After World War I, he traveled around the world; his excursions included a famous trip that delivered relief to some parts of famine-ridden Russia. Although millions perished in Russia during the war, Nansen is said to be responsible for saving at least 7 million people, most of whom were children, by arranging for aid from the international community. In 1921, he was made high commissioner for refugees in the League of Nations. His work in this position, aiding war victims, won him the Nobel Prize in 1922.

Nansen wrote several volumes, including *Eskimo Life* (1893), *Closing-nets for Vertical Hauls and for Vertical Towing* (1915), *Russia and Peace* (1923), and *Armenia and the Near East* (1928). He grew up in Frøen, just outside of Christiania, Norway. He received his doctorate in zoology from the University of Christiania in 1888 after being captivated by the Arctic and its solitude. This fascination and an insatiable drive to explore inspired him to cross Greenland on skis with a small party that same year (Christophersen 1961).

Arvid Pardoe (1914–1999)

According to Arvid Pardoe's famous "common heritage" idea, some resources should be commonly held and controlled by everyone on Earth, in contrast to private and open resources that are often controlled by the most powerful. The common heritage ethic further argues that these commonly held resources should be developed and used to fund humanitarian work worldwide.

Pardoe was the UN ambassador for Malta, and he first urged the common heritage idea on the international community in 1969. At that time, he made a speech to the General Assembly that moved the United Nations to unanimously adopt Resolution 2749 (XXV) on December 17, 1970. This document declared that seabed resources under the high seas are the "common heritage of mankind." However, it left unclear exactly where the high seas started or stopped, and thus, the third Law of the Sea Convention was called to settle the dispute.

Pardoe also advocated for an international agency to manage the leasing of the seabed and subsoil; he also argued for using the ocean's resources for "peaceful purposes." Both of these provisions were maintained in the final UNCLOS treaty, making Pardoe the parent of at least three critical aspects of the world's interaction with the ocean at this time.

When he passed away, Pardoe was remembered as the father of the Law of the Sea and as a "visionary who had a decisive influence" on all contemporary work on the ocean regime (United Nations 1999). Ironically, mining deep-seabed minerals, such as manganese nodules, still does not occur because the process is too expensive. Consequently, the International Seabed Authority (ISA) has not passed on to developing nations the windfall that Pardoe had once imagined.

Santa Barbara Oil Blowout (1969)

Beginning on January 28, 1969, an oil well in the Santa Barbara Channel near Santa Barbara, California, erupted uncontrollably for ten days. The spill was caused by the Union Oil drilling operation that fractured an oil field under the channel. Since the spill was from a fracture at the bottom of the ocean floor and not at the point of the well, it had to be contained underneath the ocean floor. This was accomplished by pumping cement into and below the fracture to plug the rupture.

The event came less than a year after the *Torrey Canyon* spill (see chapter 2). Ironically, the *Torrey Canyon* was owned by a subsidiary of Union Oil, and the tanker had received its name from a Santa Barbara oil field.

One effect of the *Torrey Canyon* spill was that it inspired contingency plans, to be required by the federal government, for dealing with local oil spills. The National Contingency Plan was designed to coordinate agencies in case of an oil spill; the agencies were supposed to be organized around regional plans tailored for each area. But Santa Barbara's regional plan was not up-to-date with the new plan. As a result, the cleanup was fraught with delays, mistakes, unsuccessful experiments, and poor communication that extended the disaster for many days. Oil stretched for miles along the California coast, and poisonous gas clouded the area as it bubbled up with the crude.

No sooner was the blowout said to be contained than a second spill was reported. Union Oil officials admitted to knowing about the second spill two days earlier, but they did not report it. With the second blowout in the same area, oil spilled out of the sea floor with little interruption from the end of January until the beginning of March 1968.

Given the continued mistakes during cleanup and the appalling fact that there was a third Union Oil spill in December 1969 in the same area, the Santa Barbara blowout sparked opposition to all oil drilling in the channel. Nevertheless, a federal commission would study the question and find that drilling there was appropriate.

United Nations Conference on Environment and Development (1992)

The United Nations Conference on Environment and Development (UNCED) is also known as the Rio Conference (after the location where it was held) and as the "Earth Summit." Although it was the second conference of its type on the planet's environmental condition as a whole, it is usually described as more important than its counterpart, the United Nations Conference on the Human Environment (held in Stockholm, Sweden), because UNCED was more widely attended and received more international legitimacy.

The Rio and Stockholm efforts both worked to answer the same question of "how to respond to urgent environmental problems in a politically, economically and culturally divided world" (Conca and Dabelko 1998, 6). The most important agreement to come out of Rio was Agenda 21, a massive document guiding practical environmental management into the twenty-first century. For the oceans, the critical part of that document was Chapter 17 of Agenda 21, "Protection of the Oceans, All Kinds of Seas, Including Enclosed and Semi-enclosed Seas, and Coastal Areas and the Protection, Rational Use and Development of Their Living Resources."

This chapter has 130 sections guiding sustainable development of ocean resources. Specific areas of guidance and agreement commit participants to using integrated coastal management (see chapter 1) and protecting marine environments; the document also calls for sustainable use of high-seas areas and areas under national jurisdiction, precautionary management techniques under conditions of uncertainty, and strengthening international and regional cooperation and coordination of ocean conservation.

Chapter 17 utilizes both broad and specific prescriptions for ocean management by individual nations. Broad prescriptions include a call for all nations to be proactive in regard to pollution concerns and to collect specific data on inland sources of marine pollution. Another issue addressed in this chapter is the need to build the "capacity" of nations, referring to an individual nation's ability to complete its obligations to an agreement. To use integrated coastal management, for example, a nation must have the scientific and management capacity to regulate inland and offshore sources of pollution and degradation. Different nations have built up more capacity than others, depending on their history of working on a problem, their access to technology, and their available pool of expertise to help tackle the issue at hand. Chapter 17 acknowledges that wealthy nations will be expected to help pay for capacity building in poorer nations if the global oceans are to be managed with relative parity (United Nations 1992).

Chapter 17 and Agenda 21 as a whole capture some of the most important sentiments regarding ocean management in recent history. Although varying degrees of obligation surround the challenges posed by Agenda 21, it is important to recognize that an agreement with such wide adherence and visibility lends vital support to primary principles of ocean conservation.

Year of the Ocean (1998)

The United Nations, which occasionally chooses a year-long theme, declared 1998 to be the Year of the Ocean. The purpose of this declaration was to highlight global dependence on the ocean and promote respect for its health. This event was both rare and remarkable in that it was an effort to recognize the totality of dependence and connection that all life has to the ocean and accordingly establish proactive international, national, and local policies.

The declaration notes that 90 percent of all living entities, including three-quarters of the human population, exist near a coast. It states that life itself was born in the ocean and reaffirms that, without the ocean, life would not be possible. Thus, the Year of the Ocean was focused on supporting sustainable development of the ocean's resources, respecting international agreements such as the Law of the Sea, and using temperance in the face of projected scarcity in order to limit human conflict over ocean resources.

The United Nations promoted the educational use of the Year of the Ocean curriculum. Materials were geared to teach students about the basic functions of the ocean and the need to protect the marine environment (Mayer 1998). The Year of the Ocean also demonstrated that more research and human interest should be focused on the ocean. Even in the twenty-first century, the ocean is a dramatic mystery, and most of its functions and ecological complexities remain unknown. Moreover, some 95 percent of the ocean remains unexplored. On this point, the United Nations requested that nations dedicate more resources to studying and understanding the ocean. The oceans are changing dramatically: surface temperatures and currents are shifting (perhaps as a function of global warming), fish stocks are in decline, and pollution is high. The Year of the Ocean was intended to bring attention to these changes and ask governments and global citizens to take notice and protect the ocean world.

The event was well publicized and had many participants. However, as the remaining links to the program are updated and references continue to be made about the Year of the Ocean, it is clear that one year is not sufficient for the task at hand. To be effective in governing the oceans in a sustainable manner, attention, research, and care for the ocean must be a continuing tradition.

References

American Academy of Achievement. 2001. "Dr. Sylvia Earle, Undersea Explorer, Biography." Available online at http://www.achievement. org/autodoc/page/ear0bio-1. Accessed on November 20, 2002.

Christophersen, Chr. A. R. 1961. *Fridtjof Nansen: A Life in the Service of Science and Humanity.* Originally published by the United Nations High Commissioner for Refugees and the Norwegian Refugee Council in collaboration with the Cultural Office of the Norwegian Ministry of Foreign Affairs. Available online at http://www.fni.no/christ.htm. Accessed on November 20, 2002.

Conca, Ken, and Geoffrey Dabelko, eds. 1998. *Green Planet Blues.* 2nd ed. Boulder, CO: Westview Press.

Cousteau Society. 2001. "Cousteau People: Jacques-Yves Cousteau, Founder." Available online at http://www.cousteausociety.org/ tcs_people.html. Accessed on November 20, 2002.

Deacon, Margaret. 1997. *Scientists and the Sea 1650–1900: A Study of Marine Science.* Brookefield, VT: Ashgate Publishing.

Government of Canada. 1996. "The History of the Northern Cod Fishery." Available online at http://collections.ic.gc.ca/cod/ collapse.htm. Accessed on November 20, 2002.

Governments of Newfoundland and Labrador. 2001. "The Past Century." Available online at http://www.gov.nf.ca/fishaq/industry/past.htm. Accessed on November 20, 2002.

Grotius, Hugo. 1972. *The Freedom of the Seas, Or, The Right Which Belongs to the Dutch to Take Part in the East Indian Trade,* reprint ed. New York: Arno Press.

Hodge, Robert. 2002. "Matthew Fontaine Maury: Pathfinder of the Seas." In *Historypoint.org.* Available online at http://www.historypoint.org. Accessed on November 20, 2002.

Littlefield, Angie. 1997. "Minamata Disaster." *Trade and Environment Database.* Available online at http://www.american.edu/TED/MINA-MATA.HTM. Accessed on November 20, 2002.

Lynn-Jones, Sean M. 1993. "Agreements to Prevent Incidents at Sea and Dangerous Military Activities: Potential Applications in the Asia-Pacific Region." In A. Mack, ed., *A Peaceful Ocean? Maritime Security in the Pacific in the Post–Cold War Era.* St Leonards, New South Wales, Australia: Allen and Unwin Publishers.

Maas, Willem. 2001. "Hugo Grotius." Available online at http://pantheon.yale.edu/~wm54/grotius.htm.

Mayor, Frederico. 1997. "1998 International Year of the Ocean: Message of UNESCO Director-General." Available online at http://www.ioc.unesco.org/ivo/newsdesk/97-250e.htm. Accessed on August 20, 2002.

United Nations. 1992. "Protection of the Oceans, All Kinds of Seas, Including Enclosed and Semi-enclosed Seas, and Coastal Areas and the Protection, Rational Use and Development of Their Living Resources." In *Report of the United Nations Conference on Environment and Development.* Available online at http://www.un.org/esa/sustdev/agenda21chapter17.htm. Accessed on November 20, 2002.

———. 1999. Press Release of July 16. "Dr. Arvid Pardo, 'Father of Law of Sea Conference,' Dies at 85, in Houston, Texas." Available online at http://www.un.org/News/Press/docs/1999/19990716.SEA1619.html. Accessed on November 20, 2002.

Uzgalis, Bill. 1999. "Hugo Grotius 1583–1645." Available online at http://www.orst.edu/instruct/phl302/philosophers/grotius.html. Accessed on November 20, 2002.

6

Statistics and Data

In this chapter, data about ocean politics and policy will be presented. The first section provides country data on coastlines, membership in the Law of the Sea Treaty, and participation in the Regional Seas Programme. Next, fishing data are listed, including facts on the amount of fish caught in the world over time, how that fish is used, the top fish-consuming nations, the countries with the highest per capita (per person) intake of fish, the top fish-importing and fish-exporting countries, and a list of U.S. regional fishery management councils. Finally, data are provided on the importance and condition of coastal ecosystems. This material includes marine economic values and lists of both U.S. marine protected areas and UN World Heritage marine protected areas. Also available in this part is a profile of three key coastal indicators: global mangroves, global sea grasses, and global coral reefs. The final section in this chapter presents a list of threatened marine life. This section also gives details on extinct marine species, whale populations, and the extent of exceptions to the current ban on whaling. The reasons for including each set of data are also offered, together with an explanation of the particular set's importance.

Country Data: Coastlines, Membership in the Law of the Sea Treaty, and Participation in the Regional Seas Programme

Member States of the United Nations and Length of Their Coastlines

Table 6.1 serves two purposes. First, it provides an accurate list of all the countries in the United Nations as of 2000. Second, it demonstrates the tangible ocean interest each nation has as measured by the length of its coastline. A zero entry for coastline length indicates a landlocked nation. Although landlocked countries are supposed to receive special privileges enabling them to gain access to the ocean through their neighbors' territories, they are typically at a geographic disadvantage in terms of commerce and wealth accumulation. Countries with long coastlines, by contrast, generally have an advantage, assuming that there are good locations for establishing ports on those coasts (sometimes, there is no good place for a port due to shallow water, clifflike coastlines, or other problems). However, a long coastline can also be a disadvantage, as it is for some island nations who have trouble controlling this type of border (for example, in guarding it from drug traffickers and other threats). Note that in this table, "n/a" means "not available": many of the nations with this designation are newly independent, and their coastline data are not available because their coastal assets were previously contained within the colonial nations that controlled them. Table 6.2 aggregates the national data to demonstrate the global concentrations of coastline, with the understanding that more coastline means more access to global markets, more marine resources, and more protection from military attack.

Countries That Are Parties to the 1982 United Nations Convention on the Law of the Sea

Table 6.3 shows which countries have become parties to the 1982 Law of the Sea. In some cases, as with the United States, a country signed the treaty but did not become a party because its legislature did not approve, or ratify, the signing. This is an important list because the Law of the Sea is the primary international ocean law, and these nations have said they bind themselves to this widely held agreement. Political disagreement about adhering to a treaty can be volatile. Consider the case of Turkey. It did not become a party because it felt that Law of the Sea boundaries would primarily aid its rival, Greece. Thus, Turkey not only has abstained from the treaty but also has said that if Athens, which is a party to UNCLOS, declares Law of the Sea economic boundaries, it will go to war with Greece.

United Nations Regional Seas Programme Data

The United Nations Regional Seas Programme is one of the most successful diplomatic agreements for the environment because it has allowed political rivals to become members of a cooperative plan for the ocean. Table 6.4 shows how the programme divides up the regions of the world. In addition, a list of nations that participate in regional plans is provided in this table. This list includes information on formal treaties that are in force; such treaties indicate a higher level of commitment to the plan than informal agreements. Action plans and conventions represent differing levels of commitment. The absence of an action plan may denote a low degree of commitment to the programme, whereas the presence of a convention may denote more commitment to the programme than if there is an action plan but no binding convention to ensure that it is implemented. For more information on this programme, e-mail http://water@unep.org.

Fishing

Fishing is one of the most important activities on the ocean, particularly in economic terms. Because of this, fish information is well documented. The first data set (Table 6.5) provided here indicates the amount of fish caught in the ocean and in aquaculture settings. These figures are very significant because they show at least two things. First, they show how many fish are available for people to eat and use for other purposes. Second, they indicate world trends over time in terms of how many fish are being caught. Since the 1970s, fishing effort has doubled as measured by the number of fishers, but fish catch levels are declining in the wild. In other words, twice as much effort is being used to catch the same or fewer fish, which implies that it is harder to catch fish now than in earlier years. It is assumed that one reason for this is because there must be much fewer fish to catch. How this fish stock is used is shown in Table 6.6.

Also provided is a breakdown of aquaculture (farmed fish) trends (Table 6.5). This demonstrates the increasing importance of aquaculture for world fish catches. Aquaculture has increased a great deal over time, but so has the controversy surrounding it, including the problems of escaped cultured fish that mingle with wild fish (a problem of biodiversity), pollution from concentrated areas that receive tremendous amounts of food and fertilizer in order to culture the fish, and the fact that the food that is fed to aquaculture fish is actually processed wild fish.

Note that, as shown in Table 6.5 and Figure 6.1, the role of aquaculture in the world fish catch doubled from 1990 to 1999 and that the greatest amount of fish caught in the ocean occurred in 1997 (86.3 million tons). The amount of wild fish caught has since gone down to 1995 levels.

The countries that are most involved in fishing are shown by their aggregate consumption per nation, by highest per capita consumers, and by top fish-importing and fish-exporting countries in Tables 6.7, 6.8, and 6.9. These data are important simply because they reflect the level of dependence on fishing. Table 6.10 is a summary of U.S. states that participate in the regional fisheries of the United States. This would be the first piece of information necessary to do research on a particular state's involvement in U.S. fishery management.

Marine Oil Pollution Data

Table 6.11 documents marine oil pollution. Note that the figures presented here are estimates, since oil pollution worldwide is underdocumented. The large increase in numbers relating to natural oil pollution that seeps through cracks in the ocean floor is probably due to the availability of better information on the subject. There are about 294 gallons (or 7 barrels) in 1 ton of oil, which is useful to know because oil pollution data are typically reported in tons; however, this is an average, since the weight of the oil depends on its level of refinement (for example, gasoline contains 333 gallons per ton). Note that 1 gallon of oil can contaminate a million gallons of seawater. Also note that the apparent increase in oil pollution caused by natural seeps may actually reflect a better understanding of this phenomenon and does not necessarily represent a 200 percent increase.

Coastal Ecosystem Health

Economic Values of the Ocean

The task of placing economic values on the environmental goods and services that provide the foundation for life itself is not without its hazards. However, experts in the field of ecological economics, a branch of economics that takes on that task, argue that *not* placing an economic value on our environmental benefits is also a dangerous proposition because we may take them for granted, especially in a world that is increasingly driven by economic interests. Table 6.12 lists some of the values that have been ascribed to ocean goods and services by ecological economists and other ocean experts. Note that the coastal environments that cover only a little more than 6 percent of the earth produce more than 41 percent of the value of the world ecosystem's goods and services. Combined with the threats that face these ecosystems (see the information on sea grasses, coral reefs, and mangroves later in this chapter), this situation presents a serious economic threat and reinforces the notion that good ocean management is a very real security matter.

Marine Protected Areas (MPAs)

A marine area may enjoy several levels of protection, such as no-fishing zones or zones where other extractive activities are prohibited, bans or limits on developing the coastline, or reserves for scientific research, to name just a few. MPAs also have varying degrees of commitment from the governments that declare them; some MPAs are suspected of being protected in name only, lacking funding or enforcement. Such areas are referred to as "paper parks." Paper parks are suspected to exist all over the world, but we have no data to quantify this assumption. For that reason, all reserves are treated in the same way, even as their different goals are noted; many of these reserves, however, may be protected on paper only. Nonetheless, the distribution and area of the protection allotted to MPAs is increasing. Tables 6.13 and 6.14 compile some of the data on MPAs. They include only a small portion of the marine preserves, since there are over 3,000 MPAs globally.

Table 6.13 shows the World Heritage Sites that have "major wetland and marine values" according to the United Nations Environment Programme (1997). World Heritage Sites are areas recognized as having important contributions to make to the global community. Though no funding is attached to the designation of an area as a World Heritage Site, people across the world are encouraged to protect these locations.

Table 6.14 shows the U.S. marine protected areas. The information in this table is interesting because the number of such areas is very small compared to the hundreds of wilderness areas, parks, national forests, and other federally protected areas in the country. Also note that most of these sanctuaries have only been protected since the mid-1980s and 1990s.

Mangroves

Mangroves are plant species, often trees, that are able to live with their roots exposed to saltwater. They are important because they provide protective habitats and nurseries for other marine species, such as fish. Mangroves typically occur between 30 degrees north and south of the equator (Field 2000). Table 6.15 provides general global information on the condition of mangroves. Table 6.16 lists the estimated amount of mangrove areas that have been lost. However, it is very difficult to track the loss of mangroves, since most countries do not keep such information today and very few kept it fifty years ago. Data on some select countries have been made available. Globally, only twenty countries have started mangrove restoration plans, and of that number, only nine have replanted more than 10 square kilometers (about 3 square miles).

Sea Grasses

Like coral reefs and mangroves, sea grasses provide sanctuary for marine species, and they are strong indicators of marine health. Sea grasses are perennial plants that grow under water. They are a principal component in shallow marine ecosystems such as estuaries and are continually exposed to changes in the coastal environments. Sea grasses also experience rapid and broad changes in relation to the larger changes in the sea, and for this reason, they are among the best indicators of water quality and coastal ecosystem integrity. Among the services that sea grasses provide are erosion stability and respiratory and nutrient cycling (exchanging gas and material nutrients within a system). Currently, sea grasses are in decline across the globe, most likely due to extensive coastal development. Table 6.17 lists some interesting information on sea grasses and the threats they face. Clearly, they are an essential component of the World Ocean's marine life.

Coral Reefs

Twenty-five percent of all known marine fish species use coral reefs as habitat. The potential sustainable yield of marine life from reefs could be as high as 9 million metric tons (almost 20 billion pounds), or 12 percent of the world fish catch. Some coral reefs are believed to be as much as 2.5 million years old. Threats to coral reefs include the use of cyanide and explosives to extract valuable fish (some grouper fish are worth $300 a plate), coastal development, marine and inland pollution, sedimentation (which buries coral), and the crown of thorns starfish (which consumes coral and is proliferating). These starfish have destroyed about 90 percent of Japanese coral reefs off Okinawa. Table 6.18 provides some general information regarding coral reefs, which is helpful in demonstrating the importance of the reefs to the marine environment. Table 6.19 shows the amount of shallow coral reefs per region. These reefs are the most valuable for fish and marine life as well as for scuba diving and ecological tourism. Table 6.20 notes the countries with the greatest amounts of coral reef assets, reflecting the marine riches and diversity that these countries enjoy; it also shows where coral reefs are concentrated in the greatest number. Table 6.21 lists the "World Heritage Sites with a Coral Reef" (which designates a recognition of needed protection). This information is important because it indicates the level of global concern for these particular sites.

Endangered Marine Species

The World Conservation Union Red List shows that 708 marine species are endangered in some way or have already become extinct. The loss of a species, particularly as a result of human behavior, is an extremely serious environmental threat. Beyond the ethical implications of causing a species to become extinct, many biologists and ecologists believe that each loss of a species diminishes the strength of our earthly habitat because each species provides support for others, which in turn support human existence. This web of life has been likened to an airplane and its rivets by renowned population scientists Paul and Anne Ehrlich. They note that each species, like a rivet in a plane, is important. With the loss of one rivet, the plane is still functional. But if a thousand rivets are lost, a wing may fall off. This is why a limited list of species that were or are in the balance has been included.

Table 6.22 lists some of the species that have become extinct. The fate of the Stellar's sea cow is a good example of human impact on biodiversity; these passive animals, slow and rich with meat, were hunted into extinction just a few years after scientists discovered them. Each species has a story, and some of these stories involve human tinkering. To Aldo Leopold, an early American naturalist, the only way to tinker intelligently was to save all the parts. Tables 6.22, 6.23, and 6.24 show some of the parts we have either lost or are in danger of losing in regard to marine habitats.

Marine extinctions are thought to be far more extensive than the list in Table 6.22 suggests, but this table shows some scientifically confirmed cases. Note that Tables 6.23 and 6.24 list "endangered" and "threatened" U.S. marine species. The difference in U.S. environmental policy is that "threatened" species usually have the possibility of becoming "endangered" within a generation. Thus, it is important to know not only current species that are at the brink of extinction but also those that are next in line in order to better plan for their protection.

Whale Populations

Whales receive special attention in ocean politics, probably because of their size, their typically gentle nature, and their importance to certain whaling cultures. For this reason, whale population information is provided. Note that whale population data are not like fishing data: the most up-to-date information is already years old, probably because whales can be very elusive and because the whales that are caught are usually underreported, perhaps by as much as two-thirds.

Table 6.25 lists the most recent population estimates of whale species, available from the International Whaling Commission at http://www.iwcoffice.org/Estimate.htm. Whale populations are difficult to estimate because some whales spend a great deal of time at very deep ocean depths and avoid human contact. Note that the percent of confidence involved in these population estimates is also indicated, which helps to foster a better understanding of the uncertain but fairly consistent conditions that surround whaling and whale populations. Indigenous exceptions to whaling have drawn a great deal of attention. Table 6.26 shows the groups included in the current aboriginal exception and the extent of their take they are allowed.

References

Center for International Earth Science Information Network (CIESIN). 1996–2001. *Environmental Treaties and Resource Indicators (ENTRI)*. Available online at http://sedac.ciesin.org/entri/. Accessed on November 20, 2002.

Costanza, Robert. 2000. "The Ecological, Economic, and Social Importance of the Oceans." In Charles Sheppard, ed., *Seas at the Millennium: An Environmental Evaluation*. New York: Pergamon Press.

Field, Colin. 2000. "Mangroves." In Charles Sheppard, ed., *Seas at the Millennium: An Environmental Evaluation*. New York: Pergamon Press.

GESAMP (Joint Group of Experts on the Scientific Aspects of Marine Environmental Protection). 2001. *A Sea of Troubles*. Available online at http://gesamp.imo.org/no70/index.htm. Accessed on May 30, 2002.

International Coral Reef Initiative. 1995. *The State of the Reefs.* Available online at http://www.ogp.noaa.gov/misc/coral/sor/. Accessed on November 11, 2002.

International Whaling Commission. 2000. *Estimates.* Available online at http://www.iwcoffice.org/Estimate.htm. Accessed on January 5, 2002.

———. 2002. *Conservation and Management.* Available online at http://www.iwcoffice.org/iwc.htm#Conservation. Accessed on July 5, 2002.

National Marine Fisheries Service. 2000. Personal communication from the National Marine Fisheries Service, Fisheries Statistics and Economics Division, Silver Spring, MD.

———. 2002a. "Regional Councils." Available online at http://www.nmfs.noaa.gov/councils/. Accessed on January 5, 2002.

———. 2002b. "Species Listed under the Endangered Species Act of 1973." Available online at http://www.nmfs.noaa.gov/prot_res/species/ESA_species.html. Accessed on November 21, 2002.

National Oceanic and Atmospheric Administration. 2001. National Marine Sanctuaries Program. Available online at http://www.sanctuaries.nos.noaa.gov/. Accessed on July 5, 2002.

National Research Council. 1985. *Oil in the Sea.* Washington, DC: National Academy Press.

———. 2002. *Oil in the Sea III.* Washington, DC: National Academy Press.

Phillips, Ronald, and Michael Durako. 2000. "Global Status of Seagrasses." In Charles Sheppard, ed., *Seas at the Millennium: An Environmental Evaluation.* New York: Pergamon Press.

United Nations. 2000. "List of Member States." Available online at http://www.un.org/Overview/unmember.html. Accessed on July 5, 2002.

———. 2002. "Chronological Lists of Ratifications of, Accessions and Successions to the Convention and the Related Agreements as at 12 November 2001." Available online at http://www.un.org/Depts/los/convention_agreements/htm. Accessed on November 20, 2002.

United Nations Environment Programme. 1997. "A Global Overview of Wetland and Marine Protected Areas on the World Heritage List." Available online at http://www.unep-wcmc.org/wh/reviews/wetlands/. Accessed on November 21, 2002.

———. 1999. "Regional Seas Programme." Available online at http://www.unep.org/unep/program/natres/water/regseas/regseas.htm. Accessed on July 5, 2002.

———. 2000. *Global Environmental Outlook.* London: Earthscan Publications.

United Nations Food and Agricultural Organization (FAO). 2000a. "Aquaculture Production 2000." Available online at http://www.fao. org/fi/statist/FISOFT/FISHPLUS.asp. Accessed on November 22, 2002.

———. 2000b. *State of World Fisheries and Aquaculture.* Rome: FAO.

Wilder, Robert, Mia Tegner, and Paul Dayton. 1999. "Saving Marine Biodiversity." *Issues in Science and Technology* 15, no. 3: 57–65.

World Conservation Union (IUCN). 2002. "Red List." Available online at http://www.redlist.org. Accessed on May 19, 2002.

World Resource Institute. 1998. "Reefs at Risk." Available online at http://www.wri.org/reefsatrisk/. Accessed on April 27, 2002.

———. 2000. "Pilot Analysis of Global Ecosystems." Available online at http://www.wri.org/wr2000/pdf/page_coast_005_extent.pdf. Accessed on April 27, 2002.

Table 6.1   Coastlines of the 189 Member States of the United Nations, as of 2000

Nation	Length of coastline (kilometers)	Nation	Length of coastline (kilometers)
Afghanistan	0	Egypt	5,898
Albania	649	El Salvador	756
Algeria	1,557	Equatorial Guinea	603
Andorra	0	Eritrea	3,446
Angola	2,252	Estonia	2,956
Antigua and Barbuda	n/a	Ethiopia	0
Argentina	4,989	Fiji	4,637
Armenia	0	Finland	31,119
Australia	66,530	France	7,330
Austria	0	Gabon	2,019
Azerbaijan	871	Gambia	503
Bahamas	n/a	Georgia	376
Bahrain	n/a	Germany	3,624
Bangladesh	3,306	Ghana	758
Barbados	n/a	Greece	1,547
Belarus	0	Grenada	n/a
Belgium	76	Guatemala	445
Belize	1,996	Guinea	1,641
Benin	121	Guinea-Bissau	3,176
Bhutan	0	Guyana	459
Bolivia	0	Haiti	1,977
Bosnia and Herzegovina	23	Honduras	1,878
Botswana	0	Hungary	0
Brazil	7,491	Iceland	8,506
Brunei Darussalam	n/a	India	17,181
Bulgaria	457	Indonesia	95,181
Burkina Faso	n/a	Iran (Islamic Republic of)	5,890
Burundi	0	Iraq	105
Cambodia	1,127	Ireland	6,437
Cameroon	1,799	Israel	205
Canada	265,523	Italy	9,226
Cape Verde	n/a	Jamaica	895
Central African Republic	0	Japan	29,020
Chad	0	Jordan	27
Chile	6,435	Kazakhstan	4,528
China	30,017	Kenya	1,586
Colombia	2,414	Kiribati	n/a
Comoros	n/a	Kuwait	756
Congo	205	Kyrgyzstan	0
Costa Rica	2,069	Lao People's Democratic	
Côte d'Ivoire	515	Republic	0
Croatia	5,663	Latvia	565
Cuba	14,519	Lebanon	294
Cyprus	n/a	Lesotho	0
Czech Republic	0	Liberia	842
Democratic People's		Libyan Arab Jamahiriya	2,025
Republic of Korea	4,009	Liechtenstein	0
Democratic Republic		Lithuania	258
of the Congo	177	Luxembourg	0
Denmark	5,316	Former Yugoslav Republic	
Djibouti	n/a	of Macedonia	0
Dominica	n/a	Madagascar	9,935
Dominican Republic	1,612	Malawi	0
Ecuador	2,237	Malaysia	9,323

Table 6.1 *(Cont.)*

Nation	Length of coastline (kilometers)	Nation	Length of coastline (kilometers)
Maldives	n/a	Seychelles	n/a
Mali	0	Sierra Leone	1,677
Malta	n/a	Singapore	268
Marshall Islands	n/a	Slovakia	0
Mauritania	1,268	Slovenia	41
Mauritius	177	Solomon Islands	9,880
Mexico	23,761	Somalia	3,898
Micronesia (Federated		South Africa	3,751
States of)	n/a	Spain	7,268
Monaco	n/a	Sri Lanka	2,828
Mongolia	0	Sudan	2,245
Morocco	2,008	Suriname	386
Mozambique	6,942	Swaziland	0
Myanmar	14,708	Sweden	26,384
Namibia	1,754	Syrian Arab Republic	212
Nauru	n/a	Tajikistan	0
Nepal	0	Thailand	7,066
Netherlands	1,914	Togo	53
New Zealand	17,209	Tonga	n/a
Nicaragua	1,915	Trinidad and Tobago	704
Niger	0	Tunisia	1,927
Nigeria	3,122	Turkey	8,140
Norway	53,199	Turkmenistan	1,289
Oman	2,809	Tuvalu	n/a
Pakistan	2,599	Uganda	0
Palau	n/a	Ukraine	4,953
Panama	5,637	United Arab Emirates	2,871
Papua New Guinea	20,197	United Kingdom of Great	
Paraguay	0	Britain and Northern	
Peru	2,414	Ireland	19,717
Philippines	33,900	United Republic of	
Poland	491	Tanzania	3,461
Portugal	2,830	United States of America	133,312
Qatar	n/a	Uruguay	660
Republic of Korea	12,478	Uzbekistan	1,707
Republic of Moldova	n/a	Vanuatu	n/a
Romania	696	Venezuela	2,800
Russian Federation	110,310	Vietnam	11,409
Rwanda	0	Yemen	3,149
Saint Kitts and Nevis	n/a	Yugoslavia	n/a
Saint Lucia	n/a	Zambia	0
Saint Vincent and the		Zimbabwe	0
Grenadines	n/a		
Samoa	n/a		
San Marino	n/a	*Nonmember states with observer status:*	
São Tomé and Principe	n/a	Cook Islands	n/a
Saudi Arabia	7,572	Holy See	0
Senegal	1,327	Switzerland	0

Sources: United Nations 2000; World Resource Institute 2000; Center for International Earth Science Information Network 1996–2001.

0 = no coastline

n/a = not available

Table 6.2   Coastline Length of Various Regions as Percentage of World Coastline Length of 1,634,701 Kilometers, as of 2000

Continent or region	Coastal lengths (kilometers)	Percentage of world coastline
Asia (excluding the Middle East)	288,459	17.6
Central America and Caribbean	73,703	4.5
Europe	325,892	19.9
Middle East and North Africa	47,282	2.8
North America (Canada and United States)	398,835	24.3
Oceana (Australia, Fiji, Papua New Guinea, Soloman Islands)	137,772	8.4
South America	144,567	8.8
Sub-Saharan Africa	63,124	3.8

Source: Adapted from World Resources Institute 2000.
Note: Coastline lengths are difficult to determine and should be considered estimates.

Table 6.3   Parties to the United Nations Convention on the Law of the Sea as of October 2002

Algeria (June 11, 1996)
Angola (December 5, 1990)
Antigua and Barbuda (February 2, 1989)
Argentina (December 1, 1995)
Australia (October 5, 1994)
Austria (July 14, 1995)
Bahamas (July 29, 1983)
Bahrain (May 30, 1985)
Bangladesh (July 27, 2001)
Barbados (October 12, 1993)
Belgium (November 13, 1998)
Belize (August 13, 1983)
Benin (October 16, 1997)
Bolivia (April 28, 1995)
Bosnia and Herzegovina (January 12, 1994)
Botswana (May 2, 1990)
Brazil (December 22, 1988)
Brunei Darussalam (November 5, 1996)
Bulgaria (May 15, 1996)
Cameroon (November 19, 1985)
Cape Verde (August 10, 1987)
Chile (August 25, 1997)
China (June 7, 1996)
Comoros (June 21, 1994)
Cook Islands (February 15, 1995)

Costa Rica (September 21, 1992)
Côte d'Ivoire (March 26, 1984)
Croatia (April 5, 1995)
Cuba (August 15, 1984)
Cyprus (December 12, 1988)
Czech Republic (June 21, 1996)
Democratic Republic of the Congo (February 17, 1989)
Djibouti (October 8, 1991)
Dominica (October 24, 1991)
Egypt (August 26, 1983)
Equatorial Guinea (July 21, 1997)
European Community (April 1, 1998)
Fiji (December 10, 1982)
Finland (June 21, 1996)
France (April 11, 1996)
Gabon (March 11, 1998)
Gambia (May 22, 1984)
Georgia (March 21, 1996)
Germany (October 14, 1994)
Ghana (June 7, 1983)
Greece (July 21, 1995)
Grenada (April 25, 1991)
Guatemala (February 11, 1997)
Guinea (September 6, 1985)
Guinea Bissau (August 25, 1986)
Guyana (November 16, 1993)
Haiti (July 31, 1996)

Table 6.3   *(Cont.)*

Honduras (October 5, 1993)
Hungary (February 5, 2002)
Iceland (June 21, 1985)
India (June 29, 1995)
Indonesia (February 3, 1986)
Iraq (July 30, 1985)
Ireland (June 21, 1996)
Italy (January 13, 1995)
Jamaica (March 21, 1983)
Japan (June 20, 1996)
Jordan (November 27, 1995)
Kenya (March 2, 1989)
Kuwait (May 2, 1986)
Lao People's Democratic Republic
   (June 5, 1998)
Lebanon (January 5, 1995)
Luxembourg (October 5, 2000)
Former Yugoslav Republic of
   Macedonia (August 19, 1994)
Madagascar (August 22, 2001)
Malaysia (October 14, 1996)
Maldives (September 7, 2000)
Mali (July 16, 1985)
Malta (May 20, 1993)
Marshall Islands (August 9, 1991)
Mauritania (July 17, 1996)
Mauritius (November 4, 1994)
Mexico (March 18, 1983)
Micronesia (Federated States of) (April
   29, 1991)
Monaco (March 20, 1996)
Mongolia (August 13, 1996)
Mozambique (March 13, 1997)
Myanmar (May 21, 1996)
Namibia (April 18, 1983)
Nauru (January 23, 1996)
Nepal (November 2, 1998)
Netherlands (June 28, 1996)
New Zealand (July 19, 1996)
Nicaragua (May 3, 2000)
Nigeria (August 14, 1986)
Norway (June 24, 1996)
Oman (August 17, 1989)
Pakistan (February 26, 1997)
Palau (September 30, 1996)
Panama (July 1, 1996)
Papua New Guinea (January 14, 1997)

Paraguay (September 26 , 1986)
Philippines (May 8, 1984)
Poland (November 13, 1998)
Portugal (November 3, 1997)
Republic of Korea (January 29, 1996)
Romania (December 17, 1996)
Russian Federation (March 12, 1997)
Saint Kitts and Nevis (January 7, 1993)
Saint Lucia (March 27, 1985)
Saint Vincent and the Grenadines
   (October 1, 1993)
Samoa (August 14, 1995)
São Tomé and Principe (November 3,
   1987)
Saudi Arabia (April 24, 1996)
Senegal (October 25, 1984)
Seychelles (September 16, 1991)
Sierra Leone (December 12, 1994)
Singapore (November 17, 1994)
Slovakia (May 8, 1996)
Slovenia (June 16, 1995)
Solomon Islands (June 23, 1997)
Somalia (July 24, 1989)
South Africa (December 23, 1997)
Spain (January 15, 1997)
Sri Lanka (July 19, 1994)
Sudan (January 23, 1985)
Suriname (July 9, 1998)
Sweden (June 25, 1996)
Togo (April 16, 1985)
Tonga (August 2, 1995)
Trinidad and Tobago (April 25, 1986)
Tunisia (April 24, 1985)
Uganda (November 9, 1990)
Ukraine (July 26, 1999)
United Kingdom of Great Britain and
   Northern Ireland (July 25, 1997)
United Republic of Tanzania
   (September 30, 1985)
Uruguay (December 10, 1992)
Vanuatu (August 10, 1999)
Vietnam (July 25, 1994)
Yemen (July 21, 1987)
Yugoslavia (March 12, 2001)
Zambia (March 7, 1983)
Zimbabwe (February 24, 1993)

Source: Adapted from United Nations 2002.

Note: Date listed is the date of ratification of or accession or succession to the convention (when the country became an official party).

Table 6.4   13 Regions of the World as Divided by the United Nations Regional Seas Programme

Region	Nations in region	Action plan	Convention
West and Central Africa	Angola, Benin, Cameroon, Cape Verde, Congo, Côte d'Ivoire, Equatorial Guinea, Gabon, Gambia, Ghana, Guinea, Guinea-Bissau, Liberia, Mauritania, Namibia, Nigeria, São Tomé and Principe, Sierra Leone, and Togo	Adopted 1981	Abidjan Convention 1981
Red Sea and Gulf of Aden	Egypt, Eritrea, Jordan, Saudi Arabia, Somalia, Sudan, and Yemen	Adopted 1982	Jeddah Convention 1982
Northwest Pacific	China, Democratic Republic of Korea, Japan, Republic of Korea, and Russian Federation	No	No
South Pacific	Argentina, Brazil, and Uruguay	Adopted 1982	Noumea Convention 1982
Southwest Pacific	Australia, Cook Islands, Federated States of Micronesia, Fiji, France, Kiribati, Nauru, New Zealand, Niue, Palua, Papua New Guinea, Republic of the Marshall Islands, Solomon Islands, Tonga, Tuvalu, United Kingdom, United States of America, Vanuatu, and Western Samoa	Adopted 1982	Noumea Convention 1982
Caribbean	Belize, Colombia, Cuba, Guatemala, Honduras, Jamaica, Mexico, Nicaragua, Saint Lucia, Tobago, Trinidad, United States of America, and Venezuela	Adopted 1981	Cartegena Convention 1986
Eastern Africa	Comoros, France (La Réunion), Kenya, Madagascar, Mauritius, Mozambique, Seychelles, Somalia, and United Republic of Tanzania	Adopted 1993	Convention for the Protection, Management, and Development of the Marine and Coastal Environment of the Eastern African Region

Table 6.4 *(Cont.)*

Region	Nations in region	Action plan	Convention
East Asian Seas	Australia, Cambodia, China, Indonesia, Malaysia, Philippines, Republic of Korea, Singapore, Thailand, and Vietnam	Adopted 1981	No
South Asian Seas	Bangladesh, India, Maldives, Pakistan, and Sri Lanka	Adopted 1995 South Asian Cooperative Environmental Programme	No
Southeast Pacific	Chile, Colombia, Costa Rica, Ecuador, El Salvador, Honduras, Nicaragua, Panama, and Peru	Adopted 1981	Lima Convention 1981
Mediterranean	Albania, Algeria, Bosnia and Herzegovina, Croatia, Cyprus, Egypt, France, Greece, Israel, Italy, Lebanon, Libya, Malta, Monaco, Morocco, Slovenia, Spain, Syria, Tunisia, Turkey, and European Union	Adopted 1975	Barcelona Convention 1976
Kuwait Region	Bahrain, Iran, Iraq, Kuwait, Oman, Qatar, Saudi Arabia, and United Arab Emirates	Adopted 1978	Kuwait Convention 1978
Black Sea	Bulgaria, Georgia, Romania, Russian Federation, Turkey, and Ukraine	Adopted 1996	Bucharest Convention 1992

Source: United Nations Environment Programme 1999.

Table 6.5   World Aquaculture and Commercial Catches, 1990–1999 (in metric tons)

Year	World aquaculture		World commercial catch		
	Marine	Total*	Marine	Total†	Grand Total‡
1990	4,995,719	13,074,328	79,101,299	85,552,558	98,626,886
1991	5,371,579	13,740,038	78,332,030	84,544,690	98,284,728
1992	6,123,867	15,427,279	79,268,731	85,418,193	100,845,472
1993	7,333,308	17,834,912	80,055,436	86,588,466	104,423,378
1994	8,687,421	20,763,869	84,866,032	91,585,883	112,349,752
1995	10,449,864	24,493,044	84,606,586	91,871,294	116,364,338
1996	10,856,257	26,747,358	86,133,131	93,531,007	120,278,365
1997	11,242,532	28,728,165	86,260,651	93,766,336	122,494,501
1998	12,134,859	30,793,501	78,984,128	86,933,121	117,726,622
1999	13,287,441	33,310,349	84,606,398	92,866,553	126,176,902

Source: United Nations Food and Agricultural Organization 2000b.

* Total of marine and freshwater catches
† Total of marine and freshwater catches
‡ Total of world aquaculture and world commercial catches

Table 6.6 Disposition (purpose) of World Aquaculture and Commercial Fish Catches, 1995–1999 (percent of total)

Item	1995*	1996	1997	1998	1999
Marketed fresh	29.9	31.3	34.2	35.5	35.3
Frozen	23.0	22.7	22.4	23.2	21.6
Canned	11.3	10.8	10.9	11.3	10.8
Cured	10.1	10.0	9.2	9.9	9.3
Reduced to meal and oil†	24.0	23.4	21.5	18.3	21.0
Miscellaneous	1.7	1.8	1.8	1.8	2.0

Source: Table taken from National Marine Fisheries Service 2000.

* Data for 1995 to 1998 are revised. Data for marine mammals and aquatic plants are excluded.

† Only whole fish destined for the manufacture of oils and meals are included. Raw material for reduction derived from fish primarily destined for marketed fresh, frozen, canned, cured, and miscellaneous purposes is excluded; such waste quantities are included under the other disposition channels.

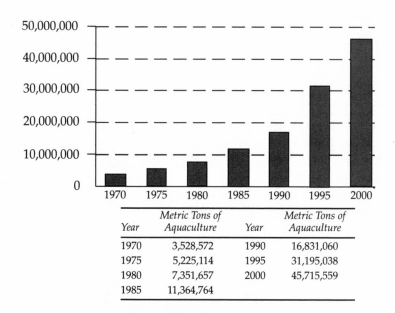

Year	Metric Tons of Aquaculture	Year	Metric Tons of Aquaculture
1970	3,528,572	1990	16,831,060
1975	5,225,114	1995	31,195,038
1980	7,351,657	2000	45,715,559
1985	11,364,764		

Figure 6.1 Growth of Aquaculture, 1970–2000

Source: United Nations Food and Agricultural Organization 2000a.

Table 6.7   The Five Nations That Consume the Most Fish and Fishery Products

Nation	Approximate average consumption from 1995–1997 (million pounds)
China	58,000
Japan	19,000
United States	12,000
India	10,000
Indonesia	9,000

Source: National Marine Fisheries Service 2000.

Table 6.8   Countries with a per Capita Fish Consumption of 100 Pounds per Year or More

Nation	Average per capita consumption (pounds/year)
Cook Island	119.3
Faeroe Islands	189.8
French Polynesia	139.8
Gabon	104.7
Guyana	121.9
Hong Kong	124.8
Iceland	200.8
Japan	152.1
Kiribati	163.6
Maldives	374.3
Niue	124.1
Norway	110.5
Palau	225.8
Portugal	131.8
Seychelles	143.1
South Korea	112.9
St. Helena	150.1
Tokelau	336.2
Western Samoa	122.4
World Average	34.6

Source: Adapted from National Marine Fisheries Service 2000.

Table 6.9 Fish Imports and Exports, by Leading Countries, 1995–1999 (thousands of U.S.$)

Country	1995	1996	1997	1998	1999
Imports:					
Japan	17,853,481	17,023,945	15,539,507	12,826,543	14,748,712
United States	7,141,428	7,080,411	8,138,840	8,578,766	9,407,307
Spain	3,105,684	3,134,893	3,069,601	3,545,751	3,286,831
France	3,221,298	3,194,133	3,062,051	3,505,333	3,280,940
Italy	2,281,316	2,590,985	2,571,868	2,808,587	2,728,568
Germany	2,478,817	2,542,957	2,362,914	2,623,741	2,288,523
United Kingdom	1,910,091	2,065,025	2,141,619	2,384,028	2,276,998
Denmark	1,573,732	1,618,669	1,521,181	1,704,234	1,771,500
Hong Kong	1,831,511	1,928,143	2,096,894	1,611,747	1,593,661
Canada	1,034,070	1,158,864	1,129,210	1,194,583	1,338,973
Other countries	13,687,212	14,920,464	15,027,372	14,301,148	14,802,483
Total	56,118,640	57,258,489	56,661,057	55,084,461	57,524,496
Exports:					
Thailand	4,449,457	4,117,865	4,329,541	4,031,279	4,109,860
Norway	3,122,662	3,415,696	3,399,229	3,661,174	3,764,790
China	2,835,021	2,856,986	2,937,281	2,656,117	2,959,530
United States	3,383,589	3,147,858	2,850,311	2,400,338	2,945,014
Denmark	2,459,629	2,698,976	2,648,911	2,897,707	2,884,334
Canada	2,314,413	2,291,261	2,270,725	2,265,236	2,617,759
Taiwan	1,809,166	1,762,132	1,779,800	1,579,836	1,763,572
Netherlands	1,447,239	1,470,046	1,425,544	1,364,809	1,744,665
Chile	1,704,260	1,697,211	1,781,805	1,596,800	1,696,819
Spain	1,190,676	1,447,170	1,471,306	1,529,315	1,604,237
Other countries	27,002,622	27,892,294	28,525,781	27,205,430	26,787,310
Total	51,718,734	52,797,495	53,420,234	51,188,041	52,877,890

Source: Table taken from National Marine Fisheries Service 2000.

Note: Data for 1995 to 1998 are revised. Data on imports and exports cover the international trade of 176 countries or areas. The total value of exports is consistently lower than the value of imports, probably because charges for insurance, freight, and similar expenses were included in the import value but not in the export value. The seven fishery commodity groups covered by this table are (1) fish—fresh, chilled, or frozen; (2) fish—dried, salted, or smoked; (3) crustaceans and mollusks—fresh, dried, salted, etc.; (4) fish products and preparations, whether or not in airtight containers; (5) crustacean and mollusk product preparations, whether or not in airtight containers; (6) oils and fats, crude or refined, of aquatic animal origin; and (7) meals, solubles, and similar animal foodstuffs of aquatic animal origin.

Table 6.10 Makeup of U.S. Regional Fishery Management Councils under Magnuson-Stevens Act

Council	Constituent states
New England	Maine, New Hampshire, Massachusetts, Rhode Island, and Connecticut
Mid-Atlantic	New York, New Jersey, Delaware, Pennsylvania, Maryland, Virginia, and North Carolina
South Atlantic	North Carolina, South Carolina, Alabama, and Florida
Gulf of Mexico	Texas, Louisiana, Mississippi, Alabama, and Florida
Caribbean	U.S. Virgin Islands and the Commonwealth of Puerto Rico
Pacific	California, Washington, Oregon, and Idaho
North Pacific	Alaska, Washington, and Oregon
Western Pacific	Hawaii, American Samoa, Guam, and Commonwealth of the Northern Mariana Islands

Source: National Marine Fisheries Service 2000a.

Table 6.11 Marine Oil Pollution Data Estimates, 1985 and 2002 (gallons/year)

	1985	2002
World oil production	912 billion	1.2 trillion
World oil pollution	703 million	382 million
Accidental oil spills	37 million	29 million
Cargo washing (intentional spills)	n/a	10.5 million
Pipelines (offshore)	n/a	3.5 million
Natural seeps on the ocean floor	62 million	176 million
Land-based runoff	n/a	41 million

Sources: National Research Council 1985; National Research Council 2002.
n/a = not available

Table 6.12   Approximate Value of Various Aspects of World Ocean Goods and Services

	Ascribed value
Total economic value of oceanic goods and services	$U.S.23 trillion/year
• Coastal contribution to oceanic goods and services	$U.S.13.8 trillion/year
—Sea grass/algal beds	$U.S.19,004/hectare/year
—Costs of current sea grass loss	$U.S.22.8 billion/year
—Mangrove/tidal marshes	$U.S.9,990/hectare/year
—Costs of current mangrove loss	$U.S.9.7 billion/year
—Coral reefs	$U.S.6,075/hectare/year
—Costs of current coral reef loss	$U.S.36.5 billion/year
• Open ocean/high seas	$U.S.9.2 trillion/year
Global cost of human diseases caused by ocean pollution	
• From bathing in contaminated waters	$U.S.1.6 billion/year
• From all exposures	$U.S.327.3 billion/year
U.S. costs (losses) due to overfishing	$U.S.8 billion/year
	300,000 jobs
Total economic value of goods and services offered by the planet	$U.S.16–54 trillion/year
	Average: 33 trillion/year
Percent of oceanic contribution to global goods and services	63.6 on average
Global sum of human goods and services (gross national product)	Ca. $U.S.25 trillion/year

Source: Costanza 2000; GESAMP 2001; Wilder, Tegner, and Dayton 1999.

Table 6.13   Number of World Heritage Sites with Major Wetland and Marine Values, by Region

Region	*Number of sites*
North America	4
Europe (including the Russian Federation)	8
Africa	5
Indomalayan region	7
Australia/Oceana	7
Antarctic	2
Latin America	6
Total	39

Source: United Nations Environment Programme 1997.

Table 6.14 U.S. Marine Sanctuary Units

Name	Location	Date of designation
Channel Islands	California	1980
Cordell Bank	California	1989
Fagatelle Bay	American Samoa	1986
Florida Keys	Florida	1990
Flower Garden Banks	Texas/Louisiana	1992
Grey Reef	Georgia	1981
Gulf of the Farallones	California	1981
Hawaiian Islands Humpback Whale Sanctuary	Hawaii	1992
Monterey Bay	California	1992
Olympic Coast	Washington	1994
Gerry E. Studds Stellwagon Bank	Massachusetts	1992
Thunder Bay	Great Lakes region	2000

Source: **National Oceanic and Atmospheric Administration 2001.**

Table 6.15 General Global Information on the Condition of Mangroves

Number of mangrove species known	69
Estimated global area of mangroves	182,305 km²
• South and Southeast Asia	75,688 km²
• Australasia	18,789 km²
• Americas	49,485 km²
• West Africa	27,995 km²
• East Africa and the Middle East	10,348 km²
Countries with mangroves	112
Dominant mangrove countries	
• Indonesia	42,550 km² (23.3%)*
• Brazil	13,800 km² (7.6%)
• Australia	11,500 km² (6.3%)
• Nigeria	10,515 km² (5.8%)
• Total of all four countries	78,365 km² (43%)

Source: Field 2000.

* Percentage figures indicate percentage of total mangroves in the world

Table 6.16   Loss of Mangroves in Various Countries

Country	Loss (square kilometers)
Malaysia	590
Philippines	4,367
Thailand	1,774
Vietnam	2,440
Peru	94
Ecuador	419
Total	9,684*

Source: Field 2000.
* 9,684 km² = over 5% of world total

Table 6.17   General Information on Global Condition of Sea Grasses

Documented losses of sea grass	290,000 hectares
Minimum estimated global loss of sea grass	1.2 million hectares
Typical sea grass growth rate	5–10 mm/day
Some marine animals directly dependent on sea grass	Manatees, dugongs, waterfowl, green turtles, queen conchs, and pearl oyster Many species of fish Many species of biota that live and rest on and under the grass leaves
Natural threats to sea grass	"Wasting disease," a disease specific to sea grass Some animal activity, e.g., the dugong graze on the grass and upturn the roots Some natural disasters, e.g., cyclones Changes in sunlight/solar radiation
Human threats to sea grass	Mechanical disturbances, such as from motor boats, dredging, and development Pollution, especially from oil, sewage, agrichemicals, and PCBs Rising ocean temperatures

Source: Data from Phillips and Durako 2000.

Table 6.18 General Information on Global Condition of Coral Reef

Total global coral reef area	600,000 km2
Amount of reef degraded beyond recovery	10% or 60,000 km²
Projected reef loss by 2020	40% or 240,000 km²
Total amount of reef at risk • High risk • Medium risk • Low risk	80% or 480,000 km² 27% or 67,900 km² 31% or 79,000 km² 42% or 108,400 km²

Percentage breakdown of threats to reefs	36% by overexploitation
	    (e.g., taking of living resources)
	30% by coastal development
	    (building near reefs)
	22% by inland pollution
	    (runoff of pollutants)
	12% by marine pollution
	    (direct pollution affecting reef life)

Estimated contribution of reefs to world economy	U.S.$375 billion/year
Species that use reefs as habitat • Fish • Coral • Phyla represented • Total marine species	 25% of all known fish/4,000 species 800 species described 25 out of 31 major phyla Between 1–9 million species (estimates vary)
• Total species threatened	As many as 1 million

Sources: International Coral Reef Initiative 1995; World Resource Institute 1998.

Table 6.19 Amount of Shallow Coral Reefs, by Region

Country	Loss (square kilometers)
Caribbean	20,000
Middle East	20,000
Atlantic (except Caribbean)	3,100
Indian Ocean	36,100
Southeast Asia	68,100
Pacific	108,000
Total	255,300

Sources: International Coral Reef Initiative 1995; World Resource Institute 1998.

Table 6.20 Countries with the Most Coral Reefs

Country	Area of reefs (square kilometers)	Amount under medium-high threat (square kilometers)
Australia	48,000	47,000
Indonesia	42,000	20,000
Philippines	13,000	2,000
Papua New Guinea	12,000	10,000
Fiji	10,000	8,000
Maldives	9,000	9,000

Sources: International Coral Reef Initiative 1995; World Resource Institute 1998.

Table 6.21 World Heritage Sites with a Coral Reef (designating a recognition of needed protection)

Country	Site
Australia	Wet Tropics of Queensland
	Great Barrier Reef
	Lord Howe Island Group
Belize	Belize Barrier Reef System
Indonesia	Komodo National Park
	Ujung Kulon National Park
Mexico	Sian Ka'an
Philippines	Tubbataha Reef Marine Park
Seychelles	Aldabra Atoll
United Kingdom	Henderson Island
United States	Everglades National Park

Source: United Nations Environment Programme 1997.

Table 6.22   Some Extinct Marine Species

Ship sturgeon (Aral Sea stock) (a fish)

St. Helena Bulwer's petrel (a bird)

Labrador duck

Dieffenbach's rail (a bird)

Tahiti rail (a bird)

Beluga (Adriatic Sea stock) (a fish)

Stellar's sea cow (like a manatee)

New Zealand little bittern (a bird)

Eelgrass limpet (a seagrass)

Caribbean monk seal

West Indian monk seal

West Indian seal

Foca Fraile del Caribe (a seal)

New Zealand storm-petrel (a bird)

The entire family of Assimineidae (a mollusk)

Pallass's cormorant (a bird)

Great auk (a bird)

Lord Howe swamphen (a bird)

Laysan crake (a bird)

New Zealand grayling (a fish)

St. Helena gadfly petrel (a bird)

Japanese sealion

Source: World Conservation Union 2002.

Table 6.23   Endangered Marine Species Currently Listed under the 1973 Endangered Species Act

Whales
  Blue whale
  Bowhead whale
  Fin whale
  Humpback whale
  Northern right whale
  Sei whale
  Sperm whale

Seals
  Hawaiian monk seal

Sea Turtles
  Green sea turtle
  Hawksbill sea turtle
  Kemp's Ridley sea turtle
  Leatherback sea turtle
  Olive Ridley sea turtle

Fish
  Atlantic salmon
  Shortnose sturgeon
  Steelhead trout

Mollusks
  White abalone

Source: National Marine Fisheries Service 2002b.

Table 6.24   Domestic (U.S.) Threatened Species Listed under the 1973 Endangered Species Act

Seals
  Guadelupe fur seal

Sea Lions
  Stellar's sea lion

Fish
  Chinook salmon
  Coho salmon
  Chum salmon
  Sockeye salmon
  Gulf sturgeon

Turtles
  Loggerhead sea turtle
  Olive Ridley sea turtle
  Green sea turtle

Plants
  Johnson's sea grass

Source: National Marine Fisheries Service 2002b.

Table 6.25   Whale Population Estimates

Whale species/location	Estimate dates	Population within 95 percent confidence
Minke whales		
Southern Hemisphere	1982/83–1988/89	510,000–1,140,000
North Atlantic	1987–1995	120,000–182,000
Northwest Pacific		
and Okhotsk Sea	1989–1990	12,800–48,600
Blue whales	1989–2000	400–1400
Fin whales	1969–1989	27,700–82,000
Gray whales		
Eastern North Pacific	1997/1998	21,900–32,400
Western North Pacific	2001	Less than 100
Bowhead whales	1993	6,900–9,200
Humpback whales		
Western North Atlantic	1992/1993	Less than 12,000
Southern Hemisphere	1988	5,900–16,800
Pilot whales		
Central and Eastern		
North Atlantic	1989	440,000–1,370,000

Source: These are the most recent population estimates of whale species available from the International Whaling Commission at http://www.iwcoffice.org/Estimate.htm (accessed on November 21, 2002).

Table 6.26   Indigenous Peoples Granted a Hunting Exception from the IWC

Indigenous group	Number and species currently permitted
United States: Alaskan Eskimos and native peoples of Chukotka	67 bowhead per year; occasionally gray whales
Denmark: People of Greenland	19 fin whales per year 175 minke whales per year
St. Vincent and the Grenadines	No more than 2 humpback whales per year

Source: International Whaling Commission 2002.

7

Documents

This chapter provides portions of some of the more important international ocean documents. The first document is part of the Law of the Sea, the most important global ocean accord. Two sections from this treaty are provided. One incorporates the introductory statements to the document, or the preamble. The Law of the Sea Preamble is important because it sets the tone of the rest of the rules that have been agreed on. For example, it states that the international seabed is the common heritage of humankind and that the delegates to the Law of the Sea convention wanted to create a treaty of global effect to increase international stability regarding ocean claims and conservation. The other section provided from this treaty is Part V, which explains the expectations and agreements regarding the exclusive economic zone. This is among the most important parts of the treaty because the first 200 miles of sea out from the coastlines of the world, to which this part pertains, are also the most valuable marine ecosystems for human societies, economically, socially, and scientifically.

Next, portions of the Fishery Stock Agreement are presented because this accord aims to drastically change the way fisheries are managed around the world. For an in-depth explanation of this addition to the Law of the Sea (it is a "side agreement" to that treaty), see the third chapter in this book. The preamble to this agreement is provided so that the context in which the FSA exists can be understood. Part VI addresses compliance and enforcement, which allows the boarding of foreign vessels; it is provided here because it is this section that changes the status of the high seas from an open-pool resource (managed by no one) to a common-pool resource (managed by an active community). Part

VIII is provided to suggest the possibility that fish are such a valuable resource that militarized disputes can erupt around them; Part VIII demands peaceful settlements of such disputes and contributes to international ocean security by putting in place an expectation of behavior. Though nations may fail to meet this expectation and thereby break the regime and the international law, some countries may actually abide by the expectation, which is what makes this part important.

Finally, a small portion of Chapter 17 from the United Nations Conference on Environment and Development is presented, dealing with "All Kinds of Oceans" because this large document has guided several program areas and concepts that have to do with the World Ocean. This is one chapter out of the voluminous Agenda 21, which came out of the Rio Conference, and it is important as an agreement on limits to development and expectations for international marine conservation, especially on coastlines. The preamble of this chapter to Agenda 21, as well as the program area and objectives for coastal management, are provided.

Global Ocean Accords

The United Nations Convention on the Law of the Sea (December 10, 1982)

Preamble to the Law of the Sea Treaty

The States Parties to this Convention,

Prompted by the desire to settle, in a spirit of mutual understanding and cooperation, all issues relating to the law of the sea and aware of the historic significance of this Convention as an important contribution to the maintenance of peace, justice and progress for all peoples of the world,

Noting that developments since the United Nations Conferences on the Law of the Sea held at Geneva in 1958 and 1960 have accentuated the need for a new and generally acceptable Convention on the law of the sea,

Conscious that the problems of ocean space are closely interrelated and need to be considered as a whole,

Recognizing the desirability of establishing through this Convention, with due regard for the sovereignty of all States, a legal order for the seas and oceans which will facilitate international communication, and will promote the peaceful uses of the seas and oceans, the equitable and efficient utilization of their resources, the conservation of their living resources, and the study, protection and preservation of the marine environment,

Bearing in mind that the achievement of these goals will contribute to the realization of a just and equitable international economic order which takes into account the interests and needs of mankind as a whole and, in particular, the special interests and needs of developing countries, whether coastal or land-locked,

Desiring by this Convention to develop the principles embodied in resolution 2749 (XXV) of 17 December 1970 in which the General Assembly of the United Nations solemnly declared *inter alia* that the area of the seabed and ocean floor and the subsoil thereof, beyond the limits of national jurisdiction, as well as its resources, are the common heritage of mankind, the exploration and exploitation of which shall be carried out for the benefit of mankind as a whole, irrespective of the geographical location of States,

Believing that the codification and progressive development of the law of the sea achieved in this Convention will contribute to the strengthening of peace, security, cooperation and friendly relations among all nations in conformity with the principles of justice and equal rights and will promote the economic and social advancement of all peoples of the world, in accordance with the Purposes and Principles of the United Nations as set forth in the Charter,

Affirming that matters not regulated by this Convention continue to be governed by the rules and principles of general international law,

Have agreed as follows: [followed by the rest of the text of the agreement] . . .

Part V: Exclusive Economic Zone

Article 55: Specific legal regime of the exclusive economic zone
The exclusive economic zone is an area beyond and adjacent to the territorial sea, subject to the specific legal regime established in this Part, under which the rights and jurisdiction of the coastal State and the rights and freedoms of other States are governed by the relevant provisions of this Convention.

Article 56: Rights, jurisdiction and duties of the coastal State in the exclusive economic zone

1. In the exclusive economic zone, the coastal State has:
   a. sovereign rights for the purpose of exploring and exploiting, conserving and managing the natural resources, whether living or non-living, of the waters superjacent to the seabed and of the seabed and its subsoil, and with regard to other activities for the economic exploitation and exploration of the zone, such

as the production of energy from the water, currents and winds;

b. jurisdiction as provided for in the relevant provisions of this Convention with regard to:

    i. the establishment and use of artificial islands, installations and structures;

    ii. marine scientific research;

    iii. the protection and preservation of the marine environment;

c. other rights and duties provided for in this Convention.

2. In exercising its rights and performing its duties under this Convention in the exclusive economic zone, the coastal State shall have due regard to the rights and duties of other States and shall act in a manner compatible with the provisions of this Convention.

3. The rights set out in this article with respect to the seabed and subsoil shall be exercised in accordance with Part VI.

Article 57: Breadth of the exclusive economic zone

The exclusive economic zone shall not extend beyond 200 nautical miles from the baselines from which the breadth of the territorial sea is measured.

Article 58: Rights and duties of other States in the exclusive economic zone

1. In the exclusive economic zone, all States, whether coastal or land-locked, enjoy, subject to the relevant provisions of this Convention, the freedoms referred to in article 87 of navigation and overflight and of the laying of submarine cables and pipelines, and other internationally lawful uses of the sea related to these freedoms, such as those associated with the operation of ships, aircraft and submarine cables and pipelines, and compatible with the other provisions of this Convention.

2. Articles 88 to 115 and other pertinent rules of international law apply to the exclusive economic zone in so far as they are not incompatible with this Part.

3. In exercising their rights and performing their duties under this Convention in the exclusive economic zone, States shall have due regard to the rights and duties of the coastal State and shall comply with the laws and regulations adopted by the coastal State in accordance with the provisions of this Convention and other rules of international law in so far as they are not incompatible with this Part.

Article 59: Basis for the resolution of conflicts regarding the attribution of rights and jurisdiction in the exclusive economic zone
In cases where this Convention does not attribute rights or jurisdiction to the coastal State or to other States within the exclusive economic zone, and a conflict arises between the interests of the coastal State and any other State or States, the conflict should be resolved on the basis of equity and in the light of all the relevant circumstances, taking into account the respective importance of the interests involved to the parties as well as to the international community as a whole.

Article 60: Artificial islands, installations and structures in the exclusive economic zone

1. In the exclusive economic zone, the coastal State shall have the exclusive right to construct and to authorize and regulate the construction, operation and use of:
   a. artificial islands;
   b. installations and structures for the purposes provided for in article 56 and other economic purposes;
   c. installations and structures which may interfere with the exercise of the rights of the coastal State in the zone.
2. The coastal State shall have exclusive jurisdiction over such artificial islands, installations and structures, including jurisdiction with regard to customs, fiscal, health, safety and immigration laws and regulations.
3. Due notice must be given of the construction of such artificial islands, installations or structures, and permanent means for giving warning of their presence must be maintained. Any installations or structures which are abandoned or disused shall be removed to ensure safety of navigation, taking into account any generally accepted international standards established in this regard by the competent international organization. Such removal shall also have due regard to fishing, the protection of the marine environment and the rights and duties of other States. Appropriate publicity shall be given to the depth, position and dimensions of any installations or structures not entirely removed.
4. The coastal State may, where necessary, establish reasonable safety zones around such artificial islands, installations and structures in which it may take appropriate measures to ensure the safety both of navigation and of the artificial islands, installations and structures.
5. The breadth of the safety zones shall be determined by the coastal State, taking into account applicable international standards. Such zones shall be designed to ensure that they are reasonably related to the nature and function of the artificial islands, installations or structures, and shall not

exceed a distance of 500 metres around them, measured from each point of their outer edge, except as authorized by generally accepted international standards or as recommended by the competent international organization. Due notice shall be given of the extent of safety zones.

6. All ships must respect these safety zones and shall comply with generally accepted international standards regarding navigation in the vicinity of artificial islands, installations, structures and safety zones.

7. Artificial islands, installations and structures and the safety zones around them may not be established where interference may be caused to the use of recognized sea lanes essential to international navigation.

8. Artificial islands, installations and structures do not possess the status of islands. They have no territorial sea of their own, and their presence does not affect the delimitation of the territorial sea, the exclusive economic zone or the continental shelf.

Article 61: Conservation of the living resources

1. The coastal State shall determine the allowable catch of the living resources in its exclusive economic zone.

2. The coastal State, taking into account the best scientific evidence available to it, shall ensure through proper conservation and management measures that the maintenance of the living resources in the exclusive economic zone is not endangered by over-exploitation. As appropriate, the coastal State and competent international organizations, whether subregional, regional or global, shall cooperate to this end.

3. Such measures shall also be designed to maintain or restore populations of harvested species at levels which can produce the maximum sustainable yield, as qualified by relevant environmental and economic factors, including the economic needs of coastal fishing communities and the special requirements of developing States, and taking into account fishing patterns, the interdependence of stocks and any generally recommended international minimum standards, whether subregional, regional or global.

4. In taking such measures the coastal State shall take into consideration the effects on species associated with or dependent upon harvested species with a view to maintaining or restoring populations of such associated or dependent species above levels at which their reproduction may become seriously threatened.

5. Available scientific information, catch and fishing effort statistics, and other data relevant to the conservation of fish stocks shall be contributed and exchanged on a regular basis through competent international organizations, whether subregional, regional or global, where appropriate and with participation by all States concerned, including States whose nationals are allowed to fish in the exclusive economic zone.

Article 62: Utilization of the living resources

1. The coastal State shall promote the objective of optimum utilization of the living resources in the exclusive economic zone without prejudice to article 61.
2. The coastal State shall determine its capacity to harvest the living resources of the exclusive economic zone. Where the coastal State does not have the capacity to harvest the entire allowable catch, it shall, through agreements or other arrangements and pursuant to the terms, conditions, laws and regulations referred to in paragraph 4, give other States access to the surplus of the allowable catch, having particular regard to the provisions of articles 69 and 70, especially in relation to the developing States mentioned therein.
3. In giving access to other States to its exclusive economic zone under this article, the coastal State shall take into account all relevant factors, including, *inter alia*, the significance of the living resources of the area to the economy of the coastal State concerned and its other national interests, the provisions of articles 69 and 70, the requirements of developing States in the subregion or region in harvesting part of the surplus and the need to minimize economic dislocation in States whose nationals have habitually fished in the zone or which have made substantial efforts in research and identification of stocks.
4. Nationals of other States fishing in the exclusive economic zone shall comply with the conservation measures and with the other terms and conditions established in the laws and regulations of the coastal State. These laws and regulations shall be consistent with this Convention and may relate, *inter alia*, to the following:
   a. licensing of fishermen, fishing vessels and equipment, including payment of fees and other forms of remuneration, which, in the case of developing coastal States, may consist of adequate compensation in the field of financing, equipment and technology relating to the fishing industry;
   b. determining the species which may be caught, and fixing quotas of catch, whether in relation to particular

stocks or groups of stocks or catch per vessel over a period of time or to the catch by nationals of any State during a specified period;

c. regulating seasons and areas of fishing, the types, sizes and amount of gear, and the types, sizes and number of fishing vessels that may be used;

d. fixing the age and size of fish and other species that may be caught;

e. specifying information required of fishing vessels, including catch and effort statistics and vessel position reports;

f. requiring, under the authorization and control of the coastal State, the conduct of specified fisheries research programmes and regulating the conduct of such research, including the sampling of catches, disposition of samples and reporting of associated scientific data;

g. the placing of observers or trainees on board such vessels by the coastal State;

h. the landing of all or any part of the catch by such vessels in the ports of the coastal State;

i. terms and conditions relating to joint ventures or other cooperative arrangements;

j. requirements for the training of personnel and the transfer of fisheries technology, including enhancement of the coastal State's capability of undertaking fisheries research;

k. enforcement procedures.

5. Coastal States shall give due notice of conservation and management laws and regulations.

Article 63: Stocks occurring within the exclusive economic zones of two or more coastal States or both within the exclusive economic zone and in an area beyond and adjacent to it

1. Where the same stock or stocks of associated species occur within the exclusive economic zones of two or more coastal States, these States shall seek, either directly or through appropriate subregional or regional organizations, to agree upon the measures necessary to coordinate and ensure the conservation and development of such stocks without prejudice to the other provisions of this Part.

2. Where the same stock or stocks of associated species occur both within the exclusive economic zone and in an area beyond and adjacent to the zone, the coastal State and the States fishing for such stocks in the adjacent area shall seek, either directly or through appropriate subregional or regional organizations, to agree upon the measures necessary for the conservation of these stocks in the adjacent area.

Article 64: Highly migratory species

1. The coastal State and other States whose nationals fish in the region for the highly migratory species listed in Annex I shall cooperate directly or through appropriate international organizations with a view to ensuring conservation and promoting the objective of optimum utilization of such species throughout the region, both within and beyond the exclusive economic zone. In regions for which no appropriate international organization exists, the coastal State and other States whose nationals harvest these species in the region shall cooperate to establish such an organization and participate in its work.
2. The provisions of paragraph 1 apply in addition to the other provisions of this Part.

Article 65: Marine mammals

Nothing in this Part restricts the right of a coastal State or the competence of an international organization, as appropriate, to prohibit, limit or regulate the exploitation of marine mammals more strictly than provided for in this Part. States shall cooperate with a view to the conservation of marine mammals and in the case of cetaceans shall in particular work through the appropriate international organizations for their conservation, management and study.

Article 66: Anadromous stocks

1. States in whose rivers anadromous stocks originate shall have the primary interest in and responsibility for such stocks.
2. The State of origin of anadromous stocks shall ensure their conservation by the establishment of appropriate regulatory measures for fishing in all waters landward of the outer limits of its exclusive economic zone and for fishing provided for in paragraph 3(b). The State of origin may, after consultations with the other States referred to in paragraphs 3 and 4 fishing these stocks, establish total allowable catches for stocks originating in its rivers.
3. a. Fisheries for anadromous stocks shall be conducted only in waters landward of the outer limits of exclusive economic zones, except in cases where this provision would result in economic dislocation for a State other than the State of origin. With respect to such fishing beyond the outer limits of the exclusive economic zone, States concerned shall maintain consultations with a view to achieving agreement on terms and conditions of such fishing giving due regard to the conservation

    requirements and the needs of the State of origin in respect of these stocks.

    b. The State of origin shall cooperate in minimizing economic dislocation in such other States fishing these stocks, taking into account the normal catch and the mode of operations of such States, and all the areas in which such fishing has occurred.

    c. States referred to in subparagraph (b), participating by agreement with the State of origin in measures to renew anadromous stocks, particularly by expenditures for that purpose, shall be given special consideration by the State of origin in the harvesting of stocks originating in its rivers.

    d. Enforcement of regulations regarding anadromous stocks beyond the exclusive economic zone shall be by agreement between the State of origin and the other States concerned.

4. In cases where anadromous stocks migrate into or through the waters landward of the outer limits of the exclusive economic zone of a State other than the State of origin, such State shall cooperate with the State of origin with regard to the conservation and management of such stocks.

5. The State of origin of anadromous stocks and other States fishing these stocks shall make arrangements for the implementation of the provisions of this article, where appropriate, through regional organizations.

Article 67: Catadromous species

1. A coastal State in whose waters catadromous species spend the greater part of their life cycle shall have responsibility for the management of these species and shall ensure the ingress and egress of migrating fish.

2. Harvesting of catadromous species shall be conducted only in waters landward of the outer limits of exclusive economic zones. When conducted in exclusive economic zones, harvesting shall be subject to this article and the other provisions of this Convention concerning fishing in these zones.

3. In cases where catadromous fish migrate through the exclusive economic zone of another State, whether as juvenile or maturing fish, the management, including harvesting, of such fish shall be regulated by agreement between the State mentioned in paragraph 1 and the other State concerned. Such agreement shall ensure the rational management of the species and take into account the

responsibilities of the State mentioned in paragraph 1 for the maintenance of these species.

Article 68: Sedentary species
This Part does not apply to sedentary species as defined in article 77, paragraph 4.

Article 69: Right of land-locked States

1. Land-locked States shall have the right to participate, on an equitable basis, in the exploitation of an appropriate part of the surplus of the living resources of the exclusive economic zones of coastal States of the same subregion or region, taking into account the relevant economic and geographical circumstances of all the States concerned and in conformity with the provisions of this article and of articles 61 and 62.
2. The terms and modalities of such participation shall be established by the States concerned through bilateral, subregional or regional agreements taking into account, *inter alia*:
   a. the need to avoid effects detrimental to fishing communities or fishing industries of the coastal State;
   b. the extent to which the land-locked State, in accordance with the provisions of this article, is participating or is entitled to participate under existing bilateral, subregional or regional agreements in the exploitation of living resources of the exclusive economic zones of other coastal States;
   c. the extent to which other land-locked States and geographically disadvantaged States are participating in the exploitation of the living resources of the exclusive economic zone of the coastal State and the consequent need to avoid a particular burden for any single coastal State or a part of it;
   d. the nutritional needs of the populations of the respective States.
3. When the harvesting capacity of a coastal State approaches a point which would enable it to harvest the entire allowable catch of the living resources in its exclusive economic zone, the coastal State and other States concerned shall cooperate in the establishment of equitable arrangements on a bilateral, subregional or regional basis to allow for participation of developing land-locked States of the same subregion or region in the exploitation of the living resources of the exclusive economic zones of coastal States of the subregion or region, as may be appropriate in the circumstances and on terms satisfactory to all parties. In the implementation of this

provision the factors mentioned in paragraph 2 shall also be taken into account.

4. Developed land-locked States shall, under the provisions of this article, be entitled to participate in the exploitation of living resources only in the exclusive economic zones of developed coastal States of the same subregion or region having regard to the extent to which the coastal State, in giving access to other States to the living resources of its exclusive economic zone, has taken into account the need to minimize detrimental effects on fishing communities and economic dislocation in States whose nationals have habitually fished in the zone.

5. The above provisions are without prejudice to arrangements agreed upon in subregions or regions where the coastal States may grant to land-locked States of the same subregion or region equal or preferential rights for the exploitation of the living resources in the exclusive economic zones.

Article 70: Right of geographically disadvantaged States

1. Geographically disadvantaged States shall have the right to participate, on an equitable basis, in the exploitation of an appropriate part of the surplus of the living resources of the exclusive economic zones of coastal States of the same subregion or region, taking into account the relevant economic and geographical circumstances of all the States concerned and in conformity with the provisions of this article and of articles 61 and 62.

2. For the purposes of this Part, "geographically disadvantaged States" means coastal States, including States bordering enclosed or semi-enclosed seas, whose geographical situation makes them dependent upon the exploitation of the living resources of the exclusive economic zones of other States in the subregion or region for adequate supplies of fish for the nutritional purposes of their populations or parts thereof, and coastal States which can claim no exclusive economic zones of their own.

3. The terms and modalities of such participation shall be established by the States concerned through bilateral, subregional or regional agreements taking into account, *inter alia*:

    a. the need to avoid effects detrimental to fishing communities or fishing industries of the coastal State;

    b. the extent to which the geographically disadvantaged State, in accordance with the provisions of this article, is participating or is entitled to participate under existing bilateral, subregional or regional agreements in the exploitation of living resources of the exclusive economic zones of other coastal States;

c. the extent to which other geographically disadvantaged States and land-locked States are participating in the exploitation of the living resources of the exclusive economic zone of the coastal State and the consequent need to avoid a particular burden for any single coastal State or a part of it;

d. the nutritional needs of the populations of the respective States.

4. When the harvesting capacity of a coastal State approaches a point which would enable it to harvest the entire allowable catch of the living resources in its exclusive economic zone, the coastal State and other States concerned shall cooperate in the establishment of equitable arrangements on a bilateral, subregional or regional basis to allow for participation of developing geographically disadvantaged States of the same subregion or region in the exploitation of the living resources of the exclusive economic zones of coastal States of the subregion or region, as may be appropriate in the circumstances and on terms satisfactory to all parties. In the implementation of this provision the factors mentioned in paragraph 3 shall also be taken into account.

5. Developed geographically disadvantaged States shall, under the provisions of this article, be entitled to participate in the exploitation of living resources only in the exclusive economic zones of developed coastal States of the same subregion or region having regard to the extent to which the coastal State, in giving access to other States to the living resources of its exclusive economic zone, has taken into account the need to minimize detrimental effects on fishing communities and economic dislocation in States whose nationals have habitually fished in the zone.

6. The above provisions are without prejudice to arrangements agreed upon in subregions or regions where the coastal States may grant to geographically disadvantaged States of the same subregion or region equal or preferential rights for the exploitation of the living resources in the exclusive economic zones.

Article 71: Non-applicability of articles 69 and 70

The provisions of articles 69 and 70 do not apply in the case of a coastal State whose economy is overwhelmingly dependent on the exploitation of the living resources of its exclusive economic zone.

Article 72: Restrictions on transfer of rights

1. Rights provided under articles 69 and 70 to exploit living resources shall not be directly or indirectly transferred to third States or their nationals by lease or licence, by establishing joint ventures or in any other manner which has the effect of such transfer unless otherwise agreed by the States concerned.
2. The foregoing provision does not preclude the States concerned from obtaining technical or financial assistance from third States or international organizations in order to facilitate the exercise of the rights pursuant to articles 69 and 70, provided that it does not have the effect referred to in paragraph 1.

Article 73: Enforcement of laws and regulations of the coastal State

1. The coastal State may, in the exercise of its sovereign rights to explore, exploit, conserve and manage the living resources in the exclusive economic zone, take such measures, including boarding, inspection, arrest and judicial proceedings, as may be necessary to ensure compliance with the laws and regulations adopted by it in conformity with this Convention.
2. Arrested vessels and their crews shall be promptly released upon the posting of reasonable bond or other security.
3. Coastal State penalties for violations of fisheries laws and regulations in the exclusive economic zone may not include imprisonment, in the absence of agreements to the contrary by the States concerned, or any other form of corporal punishment.
4. In cases of arrest or detention of foreign vessels the coastal State shall promptly notify the flag State, through appropriate channels, of the action taken and of any penalties subsequently imposed.

Article 74: Delimitation of the exclusive economic zone between States with opposite or adjacent coasts

1. The delimitation of the exclusive economic zone between States with opposite or adjacent coasts shall be effected by agreement on the basis of international law, as referred to in Article 38 of the Statute of the International Court of Justice, in order to achieve an equitable solution.
2. If no agreement can be reached within a reasonable period of time, the States concerned shall resort to the procedures provided for in Part XV.

3. Pending agreement as provided for in paragraph 1, the States concerned, in a spirit of understanding and cooperation, shall make every effort to enter into provisional arrangements of a practical nature and, during this transitional period, not to jeopardize or hamper the reaching of the final agreement. Such arrangements shall be without prejudice to the final delimitation.
4. Where there is an agreement in force between the States concerned, questions relating to the delimitation of the exclusive economic zone shall be determined in accordance with the provisions of that agreement.

Article 75: Charts and lists of geographical coordinates

1. Subject to this Part, the outer limit lines of the exclusive economic zone and the lines of delimitation drawn in accordance with article 74 shall be shown on charts of a scale or scales adequate for ascertaining their position. Where appropriate, lists of geographical coordinates of points, specifying the geodetic datum, may be substituted for such outer limit lines or lines of delimitation.
2. The coastal State shall give due publicity to such charts or lists of geographical coordinates and shall deposit a copy of each such chart or list with the Secretary-General of the United Nations.

Source: United Nations. 2002. United Nations Convention on the Law of the Sea. Available online at http://www.un.org/Depts/los/convention_agreements/texts/unclos/closindx.htm. Accessed on November 23, 2002.

Agreement for the Implementation of the Provisions of the United Nations Convention on the Law of the Sea of 10 December 1982 Relating to the Conservation and Management of Straddling Fish Stocks and Highly Migratory Fish Stocks

Preamble:

The States Parties to this Agreement,
    Recalling the relevant provisions of the United Nations Convention on the Law of the Sea of 10 December 1982,

Determined to ensure the long-term conservation and sustainable use of straddling fish stocks and highly migratory fish stocks,

Resolved to improve cooperation between States to that end,

Calling for more effective enforcement by flag States, port States and coastal States of the conservation and management measures adopted for such stocks,

Seeking to address in particular the problems identified in chapter 17, programme area C, of Agenda 21 adopted by the United Nations Conference on Environment and Development, namely, that the management of high seas fisheries is inadequate in many areas and that some resources are overutilized; noting that there are problems of unregulated fishing, over-capitalization, excessive fleet size, vessel reflagging to escape controls, insufficiently selective gear, unreliable databases and lack of sufficient cooperation between States,

Committing themselves to responsible fisheries,

Conscious of the need to avoid adverse impacts on the marine environment, preserve biodiversity, maintain the integrity of marine ecosystems and minimize the risk of long-term or irreversible effects of fishing operations,

Recognizing the need for specific assistance, including financial, scientific and technological assistance, in order that developing States can participate effectively in the conservation, management and sustainable use of straddling fish stocks and highly migratory fish stocks,

Convinced that an agreement for the implementation of the relevant provisions of the Convention would best serve these purposes and contribute to the maintenance of international peace and security,

Affirming that matters not regulated by the Convention or by this Agreement continue to be governed by the rules and principles of general international law,

Have agreed as follows: . . .

Part VI: Compliance and Enforcement

Article 19: Compliance and enforcement by the flag State

1. A State shall ensure compliance by vessels flying its flag with subregional and regional conservation and management measures for straddling fish stocks and highly migratory fish stocks. To this end, that State shall:
   a. enforce such measures irrespective of where violations occur;
   b. investigate immediately and fully any alleged violation of subregional or regional conservation and management measures, which may include the physical inspection of the vessels concerned, and report promptly to the State alleging the violation and the relevant

subregional or regional organization or arrangement on
the progress and outcome of the investigation;

c. require any vessel flying its flag to give information to
the investigating authority regarding vessel position,
catches, fishing gear, fishing operations and related
activities in the area of an alleged violation;

d. if satisfied that sufficient evidence is available in respect
of an alleged violation, refer the case to its authorities
with a view to instituting proceedings without delay in
accordance with its laws and, where appropriate, detain
the vessel concerned; and

e. ensure that, where it has been established, in accordance
with its laws, a vessel has been involved in the
commission of a serious violation of such measures, the
vessel does not engage in fishing operations on the high
seas until such time as all outstanding sanctions
imposed by the flag State in respect of the violation have
been complied with.

2. All investigations and judicial proceedings shall be carried
out expeditiously. Sanctions applicable in respect of
violations shall be adequate in severity to be effective in
securing compliance and to discourage violations wherever
they occur and shall deprive offenders of the benefits
accruing from their illegal activities. Measures applicable in
respect of masters and other officers of fishing vessels shall
include provisions which may permit, inter alia, refusal,
withdrawal or suspension of authorizations to serve as
masters or officers on such vessels.

Article 20: International cooperation in enforcement

1. States shall cooperate, either directly or through subregional
or regional fisheries management organizations or
arrangements, to ensure compliance with and enforcement of
subregional and regional conservation and management
measures for straddling fish stocks and highly migratory fish
stocks.

2. A flag State conducting an investigation of an alleged
violation of conservation and management measures for
straddling fish stocks or highly migratory fish stocks may
request the assistance of any other State whose cooperation
may be useful in the conduct of that investigation. All States
shall endeavour to meet reasonable requests made by a flag
State in connection with such investigations.

3. A flag State may undertake such investigations directly, in
cooperation with other interested States or through the

relevant subregional or regional fisheries management organization or arrangement. Information on the progress and outcome of the investigations shall be provided to all States having an interest in, or affected by, the alleged violation.

4. States shall assist each other in identifying vessels reported to have engaged in activities undermining the effectiveness of subregional, regional or global conservation and management measures.

5. States shall, to the extent permitted by national laws and regulations, establish arrangements for making available to prosecuting authorities in other States evidence relating to alleged violations of such measures.

6. Where there are reasonable grounds for believing that a vessel on the high seas has been engaged in unauthorized fishing within an area under the jurisdiction of a coastal State, the flag State of that vessel, at the request of the coastal State concerned, shall immediately and fully investigate the matter. The flag State shall cooperate with the coastal State in taking appropriate enforcement action in such cases and may authorize the relevant authorities of the coastal State to board and inspect the vessel on the high seas. This paragraph is without prejudice to article 111 of the Convention.

7. States Parties which are members of a subregional or regional fisheries management organization or participants in a subregional or regional fisheries management arrangement may take action in accordance with international law, including through recourse to subregional or regional procedures established for this purpose, to deter vessels which have engaged in activities which undermine the effectiveness of or otherwise violate the conservation and management measures established by that organization or arrangement from fishing on the high seas in the subregion or region until such time as appropriate action is taken by the flag State.

Article 21: Subregional and regional cooperation in enforcement

1. In any high seas area covered by a subregional or regional fisheries management organization or arrangement, a State Party which is a member of such organization or a participant in such arrangement may, through its duly authorized inspectors, board and inspect, in accordance with paragraph 2, fishing vessels flying the flag of another State Party to this Agreement, whether or not such State Party is also a member of the organization or a participant in the arrangement, for the purpose of ensuring compliance with

conservation and management measures for straddling fish stocks and highly migratory fish stocks established by that organization or arrangement.

2. States shall establish, through subregional or regional fisheries management organizations or arrangements, procedures for boarding and inspection pursuant to paragraph 1, as well as procedures to implement other provisions of this article. Such procedures shall be consistent with this article and the basic procedures set out in article 22 and shall not discriminate against non-members of the organization or non-participants in the arrangement. Boarding and inspection as well as any subsequent enforcement action shall be conducted in accordance with such procedures. States shall give due publicity to procedures established pursuant to this paragraph.

3. If, within two years of the adoption of this Agreement, any organization or arrangement has not established such procedures, boarding and inspection pursuant to paragraph 1, as well as any subsequent enforcement action, shall, pending the establishment of such procedures, be conducted in accordance with this article and the basic procedures set out in article 22.

4. Prior to taking action under this article, inspecting States shall, either directly or through the relevant subregional or regional fisheries management organization or arrangement, inform all States whose vessels fish on the high seas in the subregion or region of the form of identification issued to their duly authorized inspectors. The vessels used for boarding and inspection shall be clearly marked and identifiable as being on government service. At the time of becoming a Party to this Agreement, a State shall designate an appropriate authority to receive notifications pursuant to this article and shall give due publicity of such designation through the relevant subregional or regional fisheries management organization or arrangement.

5. Where, following a boarding and inspection, there are clear grounds for believing that a vessel has engaged in any activity contrary to the conservation and management measures referred to in paragraph 1, the inspecting State shall, where appropriate, secure evidence and shall promptly notify the flag State of the alleged violation.

6. The flag State shall respond to the notification referred to in paragraph 5 within three working days of its receipt, or such other period as may be prescribed in procedures established in accordance with paragraph 2, and shall either:

    a. fulfil, without delay, its obligations under article 19 to investigate and, if evidence so warrants, take enforcement action with respect to the vessel, in which case it shall promptly inform the inspecting State of the results of the investigation and of any enforcement action taken; or

    b. authorize the inspecting State to investigate.

7. Where the flag State authorizes the inspecting State to investigate an alleged violation, the inspecting State shall, without delay, communicate the results of that investigation to the flag State. The flag State shall, if evidence so warrants, fulfil its obligations to take enforcement action with respect to the vessel. Alternatively, the flag State may authorize the inspecting State to take such enforcement action as the flag State may specify with respect to the vessel, consistent with the rights and obligations of the flag State under this Agreement.

8. Where, following boarding and inspection, there are clear grounds for believing that a vessel has committed a serious violation, and the flag State has either failed to respond or failed to take action as required under paragraphs 6 or 7, the inspectors may remain on board and secure evidence and may require the master to assist in further investigation including, where appropriate, by bringing the vessel without delay to the nearest appropriate port, or to such other port as may be specified in procedures established in accordance with paragraph 2. The inspecting State shall immediately inform the flag State of the name of the port to which the vessel is to proceed. The inspecting State and the flag State and, as appropriate, the port State shall take all necessary steps to ensure the well-being of the crew regardless of their nationality.

9. The inspecting State shall inform the flag State and the relevant organization or the participants in the relevant arrangement of the results of any further investigation.

10. The inspecting State shall require its inspectors to observe generally accepted international regulations, procedures and practices relating to the safety of the vessel and the crew, minimize interference with fishing operations and, to the extent practicable, avoid action which would adversely affect the quality of the catch on board. The inspecting State shall ensure that boarding and inspection is not conducted in a manner that would constitute harassment of any fishing vessel.

11. For the purposes of this article, a serious violation means:

    a. fishing without a valid licence, authorization or permit issued by the flag State in accordance with article 18, paragraph 3 (a);

b.   failing to maintain accurate records of catch and catch-
related data, as required by the relevant subregional or
regional fisheries management organization or
arrangement, or serious misreporting of catch, contrary
to the catch reporting requirements of such organization
or arrangement;

c.   fishing in a closed area, fishing during a closed season
or fishing without, or after attainment of, a quota
established by the relevant subregional or regional
fisheries management organization or arrangement;

d.   directed fishing for a stock which is subject to a
moratorium or for which fishing is prohibited;

e.   using prohibited fishing gear;

f.   falsifying or concealing the markings, identity or
registration of a fishing vessel;

g.   concealing, tampering with or disposing of evidence
relating to an investigation;

h.   multiple violations which together constitute a serious
disregard of conservation and management measures; or

i.   such other violations as may be specified in procedures
established by the relevant subregional or regional
fisheries management organization or arrangement.

12.   Notwithstanding the other provisions of this article, the
flag State may, at any time, take action to fulfil its
obligations under article 19 with respect to an alleged
violation. Where the vessel is under the direction of the
inspecting State, the inspecting State shall, at the request of
the flag State, release the vessel to the flag State along with
full information on the progress and outcome of its
investigation.

13.   This article is without prejudice to the right of the flag State
to take any measures, including proceedings to impose
penalties, according to its laws.

14.   This article applies mutatis mutandis to boarding and
inspection by a State Party which is a member of a
subregional or regional fisheries management organization
or a participant in a subregional or regional fisheries
management arrangement and which has clear grounds for
believing that a fishing vessel flying the flag of another State
Party has engaged in any activity contrary to relevant
conservation and management measures referred to in
paragraph 1 in the high seas area covered by such
organization or arrangement, and such vessel has
subsequently, during the same fishing trip, entered into an
area under the national jurisdiction of the inspecting State.

15.   Where a subregional or regional fisheries management
organization or arrangement has established an alternative

mechanism which effectively discharges the obligation under this Agreement of its members or participants to ensure compliance with the conservation and management measures established by the organization or arrangement, members of such organization or participants in such arrangement may agree to limit the application of paragraph 1 as between themselves in respect of the conservation and management measures which have been established in the relevant high seas area.

16. Action taken by States other than the flag State in respect of vessels having engaged in activities contrary to subregional or regional conservation and management measures shall be proportionate to the seriousness of the violation.

17. Where there are reasonable grounds for suspecting that a fishing vessel on the high seas is without nationality, a State may board and inspect the vessel. Where evidence so warrants, the State may take such action as may be appropriate in accordance with international law.

18. States shall be liable for damage or loss attributable to them arising from action taken pursuant to this article when such action is unlawful or exceeds that reasonably required in the light of available information to implement the provisions of this article.

Article 22: Basic procedures for boarding and inspection pursuant to article 21

1. The inspecting State shall ensure that its duly authorized inspectors:
    a. present credentials to the master of the vessel and produce a copy of the text of the relevant conservation and management measures or rules and regulations in force in the high seas area in question pursuant to those measures;
    b. initiate notice to the flag State at the time of the boarding and inspection;
    c. do not interfere with the master's ability to communicate with the authorities of the flag State during the boarding and inspection;
    d. provide a copy of a report on the boarding and inspection to the master and to the authorities of the flag State, noting therein any objection or statement which the master wishes to have included in the report;
    e. promptly leave the vessel following completion of the inspection if they find no evidence of a serious violation; and

f. avoid the use of force except when and to the degree necessary to ensure the safety of the inspectors and where the inspectors are obstructed in the execution of their duties. The degree of force used shall not exceed that reasonably required in the circumstances.

2. The duly authorized inspectors of an inspecting State shall have the authority to inspect the vessel, its licence, gear, equipment, records, facilities, fish and fish products and any relevant documents necessary to verify compliance with the relevant conservation and management measures.

3. The flag State shall ensure that vessel masters:

    a. accept and facilitate prompt and safe boarding by the inspectors;

    b. cooperate with and assist in the inspection of the vessel conducted pursuant to these procedures;

    c. do not obstruct, intimidate or interfere with the inspectors in the performance of their duties;

    d. allow the inspectors to communicate with the authorities of the flag State and the inspecting State during the boarding and inspection;

    e. provide reasonable facilities, including, where appropriate, food and accommodation, to the inspectors; and

    f. facilitate safe disembarkation by the inspectors.

4. In the event that the master of a vessel refuses to accept boarding and inspection in accordance with this article and article 21, the flag State shall, except in circumstances where, in accordance with generally accepted international regulations, procedures and practices relating to safety at sea, it is necessary to delay the boarding and inspection, direct the master of the vessel to submit immediately to boarding and inspection and, if the master does not comply with such direction, shall suspend the vessel's authorization to fish and order the vessel to return immediately to port. The flag State shall advise the inspecting State of the action it has taken when the circumstances referred to in this paragraph arise.

Article 23: Measures taken by a port State

1. A port State has the right and the duty to take measures, in accordance with international law, to promote the effectiveness of subregional, regional and global conservation and management measures. When taking such measures a port State shall not discriminate in form or in fact against the vessels of any State.

2. A port State may, inter alia, inspect documents, fishing gear and catch on board fishing vessels, when such vessels are voluntarily in its ports or at its offshore terminals.
3. States may adopt regulations empowering the relevant national authorities to prohibit landings and transshipments where it has been established that the catch has been taken in a manner which undermines the effectiveness of subregional, regional or global conservation and management measures on the high seas.
4. Nothing in this article affects the exercise by States of their sovereignty over ports in their territory in accordance with international law.

Part VIII: Peaceful Settlement of Disputes

Article 27: Obligation to settle disputes by peaceful means
States have the obligation to settle their disputes by negotiation, inquiry, mediation, conciliation, arbitration, judicial settlement, resort to regional agencies or arrangements, or other peaceful means of their own choice.

Article 28: Prevention of disputes
States shall cooperate in order to prevent disputes. To this end, States shall agree on efficient and expeditious decision-making procedures within subregional and regional fisheries management organizations and arrangements and shall strengthen existing decision-making procedures as necessary.

Article 29: Disputes of a technical nature
Where a dispute concerns a matter of a technical nature, the States concerned may refer the dispute to an ad hoc expert panel established by them. The panel shall confer with the States concerned and shall endeavour to resolve the dispute expeditiously without recourse to binding procedures for the settlement of disputes.

Article 30: Procedures for the settlement of disputes

1. The provisions relating to the settlement of disputes set out in Part XV of the Convention apply mutatis mutandis to any dispute between States Parties to this Agreement concerning the interpretation or application of this Agreement, whether or not they are also Parties to the Convention.
2. The provisions relating to the settlement of disputes set out in Part XV of the Convention apply mutatis mutandis to any dispute between States Parties to this Agreement concerning the interpretation or application of a subregional, regional or

global fisheries agreement relating to straddling fish stocks or highly migratory fish stocks to which they are parties, including any dispute concerning the conservation and management of such stocks, whether or not they are also Parties to the Convention.

3. Any procedure accepted by a State Party to this Agreement and the Convention pursuant to article 287 of the Convention shall apply to the settlement of disputes under this Part, unless that State Party, when signing, ratifying or acceding to this Agreement, or at any time thereafter, has accepted another procedure pursuant to article 287 for the settlement of disputes under this Part.

4. A State Party to this Agreement which is not a Party to the Convention, when signing, ratifying or acceding to this Agreement, or at any time thereafter, shall be free to choose, by means of a written declaration, one or more of the means set out in article 287, paragraph 1, of the Convention for the settlement of disputes under this Part. Article 287 shall apply to such a declaration, as well as to any dispute to which such State is a party which is not covered by a declaration in force. For the purposes of conciliation and arbitration in accordance with Annexes V, VII and VIII to the Convention, such State shall be entitled to nominate conciliators, arbitrators and experts to be included in the lists referred to in Annex V, article 2, Annex VII, article 2, and Annex VIII, article 2, for the settlement of disputes under this Part.

5. Any court or tribunal to which a dispute has been submitted under this Part shall apply the relevant provisions of the Convention, of this Agreement and of any relevant subregional, regional or global fisheries agreement, as well as generally accepted standards for the conservation and management of living marine resources and other rules of international law not incompatible with the Convention, with a view to ensuring the conservation of the straddling fish stocks and highly migratory fish stocks concerned.

Source: United Nations Agreement for the Implementation of the Provisions of the United Nations Convention on the Law of the Sea of 10 December 1982 Relating to the Conservation and Management of Straddling Fish Stocks and Highly Migratory Fish Stocks. 2002. Available online at http://www.un.org/Depts/los/convention_ agreements/convention_overview_fish_stocks.htm. Accessed on November 23, 2002.

Chapter 17 of "Agenda 21" from the United Nations Conference on Environment and Development

Introduction: Protection of the Oceans, All Kinds of Seas, Including Enclosed and Semi-enclosed Seas, and Coastal Areas and the Protection, Rational Use and Development of Their Living Resources

17.1. The marine environment—including the oceans and all seas and adjacent coastal areas—forms an integrated whole that is an essential component of the global life-support system and a positive asset that presents opportunities for sustainable development. International law, as reflected in the provisions of the United Nations Convention on the Law of the Sea referred to in this chapter of Agenda 21, sets forth rights and obligations of States and provides the international basis upon which to pursue the protection and sustainable development of the marine and coastal environment and its resources. This requires new approaches to marine and coastal area management and development, at the national, subregional, regional and global levels, approaches that are integrated in content and are precautionary and anticipatory in ambit, as reflected in the following programme areas:

- Integrated management and sustainable development of coastal areas, including exclusive economic zones;
- Marine environmental protection;
- Sustainable use and conservation of marine living resources of the high seas;
- Sustainable use and conservation of marine living resources under national jurisdiction;
- Addressing critical uncertainties for the management of the marine environment and climate change;
- Strengthening international, including regional, cooperation and coordination;
- Sustainable development of small islands.

17.2. The implementation by developing countries of the activities set forth below shall be commensurate with their individual technological and financial capacities and priorities in allocating resources for development needs and ultimately depends on the technology transfer and financial resources required and made available to them.

Programme areas: (A) Integrated management and sustainable development of coastal and marine areas, including exclusive economic zones

Basis for action

17.3. The coastal area contains diverse and productive habitats important for human settlements, development and local subsistence. More than half the world's population lives within 60 km of the shoreline, and this could rise to three quarters by the year 2020. Many of the world's poor are crowded in coastal areas. Coastal resources are vital for many local communities and indigenous people. The exclusive economic zone (EEZ) is also an important marine area where the States manage the development and conservation of natural resources for the benefit of their people. For small island States or countries, these are the areas most available for development activities.

17.4. Despite national, subregional, regional and global efforts, current approaches to the management of marine and coastal resources have not always proved capable of achieving sustainable development, and coastal resources and the coastal environment are being rapidly degraded and eroded in many parts of the world.

Objectives

17.5. Coastal States commit themselves to integrated management and sustainable development of coastal areas and the marine environment under their national jurisdiction. To this end, it is necessary to, inter alia:

· Provide for an integrated policy and decision-making process, including all involved sectors, to promote compatibility and a balance of uses;
· Identify existing and projected uses of coastal areas and their interactions;
· Concentrate on well-defined issues concerning coastal management;
· Apply preventive and precautionary approaches in project planning and implementation, including prior assessment and systematic observation of the impacts of major projects;
· Promote the development and application of methods, such as national resource and environmental accounting, that reflect changes in value resulting from uses of coastal and marine areas, including pollution, marine erosion, loss of resources and habitat destruction;
· Provide access, as far as possible, for concerned individuals, groups and organizations to relevant information and opportunities for consultation and participation in planning and decision-making at appropriate levels.

Source: United Nations Division for Sustainable Development. 1999. Protection of the Oceans, All Kinds of Seas, Including Enclosed and Semi-enclosed Seas, and Coastal Areas and the Protection, Rational Use and Development of Their Living Resources. Available online at http://www.un.org/esa/sustdev/agenda21chapter17.htm. Accessed on November 11, 2002.

8

Directory of Nongovernmental Organizations, Research Institutes, Associations, U.S. Government Agencies, and International Agencies

Nongovernmental Organizations

Cousteau Society
870 Greenbrier Circle, Suite 402
Chesapeake, VA 23320
(800) 441-4395
E-mail: http://cousteau@cousteausociety.org
Web site: http://www.cousteausociety.org/index.html
Contact: President

The Cousteau Society was founded in 1973 by Capt. Jacques-Yves Cousteau, who was famous throughout the world for his television programs and documentary films. The Cousteau Society advocates for marine protected areas, a permanent moratorium on commercial whaling, and the conservation of fisheries. The society is well known for its work to protect Antarctica, now an international reserve, and for its expeditions to far-flung marine areas of the world to do televised research and exploration. The society is a formal observer to the International Whaling

209

Commission and has a partnership with the United Nations Educational, Scientific, and Cultural Organization (UNESCO). The organization continues to operate several vessels that navigate the world doing marine research.

Greenpeace International
Keizersgracht 176, 1016 DW
Amsterdam, Netherlands
31 (20) 523-62-22
FAX: 31 (20) 523-62-00
Web site: http://greenpeace.org.

Greenpeace is an international activist organization whose mission is to use nonviolent methods to protest and expose environmental problems and abuses. Its members have been most active and well known for their opposition to whale hunting and nuclear energy, as well as their efforts to protect seals. In the past, Greenpeace members have used publicity stunts to bring attention to their concerns. This public relations method often involves having large banners with provocative statements or merely the Greenpeace name hanging down a smokestack or off the skyscraper belonging to an offending corporation. The person doing the stunt will typically be arrested, and the whole story will end up on the evening news, thus bringing attention to the group's overall concern. Greenpeace is one organization that is credited with the moratorium on whaling by pressuring nonwhaling states to join the International Whaling Commission to vote for a ban on commercial whale hunting.

IUCN. *See* **World Conservation Union**

Oceana
2501 M Street, N.W., Suite 300
Washington, DC 20037-1311
(877) 7-OCEANA
FAX: (202) 833–2070
E-mail: http://info@oceana.org
Web site: http://www.oceana.org.
Contact: Director

Oceana is a new international nonprofit organization that advocates for all issues regarding the ecological health of the World Ocean. It was founded at the turn of the millennium by a coalition of major U.S. foundations, including the Pew Charitable Trusts, Rockefeller Brothers Foundation, Surdna Foundation, and the Turner Foundation, in response to the view that the future of ocean politics looked "bleak" unless active advocacy was launched on a comprehensive international scale. Having major backers such as these foundations means that this new organization will likely have an influential role and be a group to watch. Some of the problems the charter members are addressing are overfishing, pollution, and protecting marine habitat. Much of their work as of this writing has focused on U.S. marine policies. They continue to file opinions and organize letter and FAX drives for protection of U.S. fisheries and sea life.

Sea Shepherd Conservation Society
P.O. Box 2670
Malibu, CA 90265
(310) 456-1141
FAX: (310) 456-2488
E-mail: http://seashepherd@seashepherd.org
Web site: http://www.seashepherd.org/

The Sea Shepherd Conservation Society is often viewed as one of the more radical ocean conservation advocacy groups, since it opposes all forms of whaling, including indigenous practices, and is known for placing its ships in the way of whaling ships in order to physically block whalers from hunting.

The organization was founded by Capt. Paul Watson in an effort to create a direct action organization (Watson was also a Greenpeace founder, see the Greenpeace entry). Its primary objective is to serve as a witness to ocean law violations and problems, but members particularly focus their efforts on documenting the hunting of cetaceans. They are thought to be behind the sinking of several whaling ships.

World Conservation Union (IUCN)
28 rue Mauverney
CH-1196 Gland, Switzerland
41 (22) 9990001
FAX: 41 (22) 9990002
E-mail: http://mail@hq.iucn.org
Web site: http://iucn.org
Contact: Director General

The World Conservation Union, otherwise known as the IUCN, is one of the preeminent international nongovernmental environmental organizations, founded in 1948. The IUCN is directly involved in promoting conservation, especially in terms of protected areas such as parks and reserves. The IUCN has established a categorization of specially protected areas that is now the global standard and includes information such as recreational access, scientific research use, permitted extractive uses, and other uses that help to describe the character of a specific protected area in relation to other such areas around the world. The IUCN also has one of the more comprehensive lists of protected areas and has produced publications, such as the *United Nations List of National Parks and Protected Areas,* that give a sense of how much of the world is reserved from overexploitation.

Relatedly, the IUCN also provides lists and plans for internationally endangered species through its day-to-day operations and through publications such as *The Red Data Lists, Red List of Threatened Animals,* and *Species Action Plans.* This makes the organization's work in the area of biodiversity preservation especially important.

The IUCN has paid specific attention to marine and coastal systems where other broad international nongovernmental organizations have been less attentive. It has implemented an organization-wide program that places an emphasis on sustainable development and protection of marine areas. According to its Web site, this program includes efforts to improve "integrated marine and coastal management, coastal planning, marine protected areas, large marine ecosystems, conservation of coral reefs, seagrasses, mangroves and endangered species such as marine turtles, stakeholder involvement, co-operative management, etc." The IUCN has offices in Africa, South and East Asia, West Asia, East Europe and Central Asia, Western Europe, South America, and North America and the Caribbean, all of which can be contacted through the group's Web site.

World Wide Fund for Nature (WWF)
WWF International Membership
Avenue du Mont-Blanc
1196 Gland, Switzerland
Web site: http://www.panda.org/
Contact: Director

Founded in 1961, the WWF is one of the most influential grassroots global environmental organizations. Its primary mission, according to its Web site, is to "stop the degradation of the planet's natural environment and to build a future in which humans live in harmony with nature, by conserving the world's biological diversity; ensuring that the use of renewable natural resources is sustainable; promoting the reduction of pollution and wasteful consumption." The organization was founded by the then head of the United Nations Education, Science, and Culture Organization (UNESCO) and the World Conservation Union (IUCN, see entry), the head of Britain's Nature Conservancy, and others who had begun to see serious challenges to global survival and life on the planet.

The WWF is active in about 100 countries and is the world's largest conservation society and advocacy group. Among its priority policy areas are endangered seas, forests, and species (with great concern over marine mammals); it also works politically to reduce climate change and toxic substances. The organization believes, with strong evidence, that it has had a significant role in the development of concern over international environmental problems.

Research Institutes

Center for Coastal Studies
P.O. Box 1036
Provincetown, MA 02657
Web site: http://www.coastalstudies.org

The Center for Coastal Studies is a small but important private, nonprofit applied research organization located at the edge of Cape Cod. The center has developed rescue techniques for large whales from fishing gear, and it has provided scientific ecological data for the establishment of marine protected areas. The institute's research on aiding large whales has been used and recognized internationally. Members of this group have helped organize population assessments of the North Atlantic right whale and the humpback whale. The North Atlantic right whale is among the most endangered whales on the planet at this time, and the Center for Coastal Studies helped in creating Cape Cod Bay as a "critical habitat," an area with protection for the whale. The center is among several scientific ecological groups that are now using their data to change public policy.

Center for the Study of Marine Policy, University of Delaware
301 Robinson Hall
University of Delaware
Newark, DE 19716

(302) 831-8086
FAX: (302) 831-3668
Web site: http://www.udel.edu/CMS/csmp/index.html

What sets the Center for the Study of Marine Policy apart from other programs of its type is its involvement in international projects. Its goal is to study marine policy, and most recently, it has worked on the implementation of the Rio Conference on Environment and Development's declarations, domestic (U.S.) and international marine policy, marine aquaculture policy, biotechnology policy, and marine ecosystem management in conjunction with global information systems. However, the center and its staff are most well known for their work on integrated coastal management, and the center is the editorial home for *Ocean and Coastal Management Journal*, one of the more important ocean management scholarly publications.

Fridtjof Nansen Institute
P.O. Box 326
N-1326 Lysaker, Norway
(47) 67-11-19-00
FAX: (47) 67-11-19-10
E-mail: http://sentralbord@fni.no
Web site: http://www.fni.no/
Contact: Director

The Fridtjof Nansen Institute, named after the Nobel laureate (see chapter 5), is a research facility that focuses on the global environment and uses a multidisciplinary approach to explain international environmental problems. The institute employs some of the top international environmental scholars, who consistently publish on topics such as global fisheries and whaling. The Norway-based group also publishes the *Yearbook of International Cooperation on Environment and Development* (formerly the *Green Globe Yearbook*) (see chapter 9).

International Institute for Sustainable Development
161 Portage Avenue East, 6th Floor
Winnipeg, Manitoba R3B 0Y4
Canada
(204) 958-7700
FAX: (204) 958-7710
E-mail: http://info@iisd.ca
Web site: http://www.iisd.org/

The International Institute for Sustainable Development is a non-partisan, interdisciplinary think tank whose mission is to provide information that will provide ways to attain sustainable development, eliminate poverty, and achieve peace. It maintains offices in New York and Geneva and provides free issues of its quarterly newsletter, *Nexus*, which discusses the crossroads of poverty, the environment, and development. As noted on the group's Web site, "In spite of the nearly $30 billion the international community invested in humanitarian assistance during the 1990s, over 1,500 people died each day of that decade as a result of civil wars and natural disasters." One of the institute's long-range goals is to provide policy influence and information to reduce this problem by strengthening conservation.

International Oceans Institute of Canada, Dalhousie University
1226 LeMarchant Street
Halifax, Nova Scotia B3H 3P7
Canada
(902) 494-3879
FAX: (902) 494-1334
Web site: http://www.ioic.dal.ca
Contact: Chairperson

Founded by the legal scholar Elisabeth Mann Borgese (see chapter 5), the International Oceans Institute strives to promote the peaceful uses of the oceans. In 2000, the institute combined with the Oceans Institute of Canada to create the International Oceans Institute of Canada. The goal of this new organization is to integrate ocean management into economic development planning and to inform policymakers of the complexity of ocean relationships. The organization is housed at Dalhousie University, which has one of the leading ocean management and law schools in the world. It is also one of the few places where students can obtain a master's degree in ocean affairs and the Law of the Sea.

Scripps Institution of Oceanography
9500 Gilman Drive
La Jolla, CA 92093-0233
(858) 534-3624
FAX: (858) 534-5306
E-mail: http://siocomm@sio.ucsd.edu

Web site: http://www.sio.ucsd.edu/
Contact: Director of Scripps Communications

The Scripps Institution is a graduate research facility operated by the University of California, San Diego. According to the institution's Web site, its aim is "to be an international leader in originating basic research, in developing scientists, and in advancing the science needed in the search for a sustainable balance between the natural environment and human activity."

The institute has been operating since 1903, when it was founded through the university by William Ritter as the San Diego Marine Biological Station. Scripps has been associated with top oceanographers from its beginning. A hundred years later, the institute has grown immensely and now occupies sixty-seven buildings over 230 acres. It currently has several research facilities along the California coast as well and employs a staff of 1,200, which includes some 190 graduate students. The Scripps Institute also uses four research vessels, which typically log 100,000 nautical miles a year. An associated organization is the Scripps Oceanographic Society, which gives interested citizens a way to become involved in oceanography. This society's Web site can be found at http://sos.ucsd.edu/index.cfm.

Woods Hole Oceanographic Institute
Information Office
Co-op Building, MS #16
Woods Hole, MA 02543
(508) 289-2252
FAX: (508) 457-2180
E-mail: http://information@whoi.edu
Web site: http://www.whoi.edu
Contact: Director

The Woods Hole Oceanographic Institute is the largest private, independent oceanographic research organization in the world. It is located on Cape Cod in the town of Woods Hole, Massachusetts, and was founded in 1930. With three research surface vessels and several submersibles, the institute is able to train oceanographers while conducting marine research around the globe. Two of the submersibles that the institute has custody of were designed for military operation, the *Sea Cliff* and the *Alvin*. These subs carry three people to depths of 15,000 feet; they are among the four types of human-occupied subs that can go lower than 10,000 feet. The other three types are owned by France,

Russia, and Japan. Japan's *Shinkai* is the deepest-diving human-occupied submersible, capable of going over 21,000 feet below the ocean surface. The *Alvin* was the vessel used to discover deep-sea thermal vents and the living communities around them in 1977 (see chapter 4).

The organization receives a great deal of funding from U.S. governmental sources, including the National Science Foundation, the Office of Naval Research, and other agencies. During World War II, the organization grew to accommodate naval defense research, and it has contributed to knowledge in ecological marine systems as well as maritime military advances. Today, most of the group's research is ecological in nature, focusing on geophysics, biology, chemistry, climate, and other oceanographic disciplines. The Woods Hole Institute issues two publications, *Oceanus* and *Woods Hole Currents*; some articles from these publications are available on the Woods Hole Web site.

Associations

American Society for International Law
2223 Massachusetts Avenue, N.W.
Washington, DC 20008
(202) 939-6000
FAX: (202) 797-7133
E-mail: See Web site
Web site: http://www.asil.org
Contact: President

The American Society for International Law promotes the study and use of international law. It was founded in 1906 in the United States. It maintains "observer" status at the United Nations and has weighed in on many areas of discussion about international law. Although the goals of the association itself are of interest to ocean scholars, the sections within the society that deal with environmental law and wildlife law are particularly pertinent. Personnel in the section of international environmental law study and comment on several far-reaching topics such as sustainable development, transboundary pollution, conservation, and global common-pool resource management. The wildlife law section publishes the *Journal of International of Wildlife Law and Policy*, which routinely features scholarly research regarding international law and ocean wildlife, such as whales and other cetaceans.

At-Sea Processors Association
4039 21st West, Suite 400
Seattle, WA 98199
(206) 285-5139
E-mail: http://apa@atsea.org
Web site: http://atsea.org
Contact: President

At-Sea Processors Association is a large industry organization that represents U.S. flag catcher-processor companies in the Bering Sea. Within the Bering Sea is the pollack fishery, which is the largest U.S. fishery and produces the fish used to make imitation crab and fast-food fillets. The association's stated goals are to support marine research, sustainable development of fisheries, individual accountability, and international management of fisheries.

At-Sea has donated funds to the University of Alaska, Fairbanks School of Fisheries and Ocean Sciences to create the Pollack Conservation Cooperative Research Center. This research group conducts investigations into the effects of industry on fishing, marine mammals, and other Bering Sea ecosystem concerns. A related organization is the Pollack Conservation Cooperative, a voluntary group of major fisher-processors in the Bering Sea who have limited their catch as a way to promote corporate self-regulation. Often, industries move to regulate themselves if government is threatening to do the same as a way to maintain control of the regulatory limits that also affect profit. Some argue that this method is more efficient and desirable; opponents argue that corporations will not take the necessary steps of significant regulation without enforcement.

International Association of Ports and Harbors
5F, North Tower New Pier Takeshiba
1-11-1 Kaigan, Minato-ku
Tokyo, Japan 105-0022
E-mail: http://info@iaphworldports.org
Web site: http://www.iaphworldports.org
Contact: President

Founded in 1955, the International Association of Ports and Harbors brings the operators of most large shipping ports together as an industry alliance. These operators handle about 60 percent of the world's seaborne traffic and 95 percent of all container traffic (traffic from container ships). The association is sometimes known as the United Ports of the World, and its motto is "World peace through world trade; world trade through world ports." This motto draws on the idea that nations that trade with one another are less likely to fight and ports are an important part of this trading relationship. Among its interests are the regulation of trade, the rules for the shipping industry, and the maintenance of global commerce. As such, the association advocates through its "consultative" status (it is allowed to offer its opinion on policies that affect it) with the United Nations for policies it views as favorable to the shipping and port industry. The International Association of Ports and Harbors is also responsible for the major trade journal on world ports, *Ports and Harbors*.

International Institute of Fisheries Economics and Trade
Department of Agricultural and Resource Economics
Oregon State University
Corvallis, OR 97331-3601
E-mail: See Web site
Web site: http://www.orst.edu/Dept/IIFET/index.html
Contact: President

The International Institute of Fisheries Economics and Trade is a relatively new organization (begun in 1982) that was organized to participate in and increase understanding about economic connections to fisheries. This effort represents a larger trend within the discipline of economics entailing attempts to better understand the value of natural resources. Conference proceedings can be ordered from this professional association at its Web site.

International Marine Mammal Association
1474 Gordon Street
Guelph, Ontario N1L 1C8
Canada
(519) 767-1948
FAX: (519) 767-0284
E-mail: http://ccosgrove@imma.org
Web site: http://www.imma.org
Contact: President

The International Marine Mammal Association originated in New Brunswick, Canada, in 1974, over the result of a concern for the loss of marine mammals and degraded marine habitats. Members now generate technical papers, popular articles, and classroom material exploring the complexities of marine mammal issues. A consistent theme for association research is the relationship between pinnipeds (seals and their close relatives) and commercial fisheries. Research completed by the association is available on its Web site.

International Studies Association
324 Social Sciences
University of Arizona
Tucson, AZ 85721
(520) 621-7715
FAX: (520) 621-5780
Contact: President

The International Studies Association is one of the more important academic associations for any subject related to international affairs. Indirect and direct influences on international ocean governance are researched and presented at the group's annual conference in several areas, such as foreign policy, international security, environmental affairs, international law, comparative politics (the study of comparing international phenomena), politics and economy, and international development. Among the scholarly journals the association publishes are *International Studies Review, International Studies Quarterly,* and *International Studies Perspectives.* Environmental scholars within the association also are involved in awarding the coveted Harold and Margaret Sprout Award for the best international environmental book of the year. At least two important resources on ocean governance are found on this short list. The first is Ronald Mitchell's *Intentional Oil Pollution at Sea: Environmental Policy and Treaty Compliance* (1994). The second is Jon Van Dyke, Durwood Zaelke, and Grant Hewison's edited volume, *Freedom for the Seas in the 21st Century: Ocean Governance and Environmental Harmony* (1993) (see chapter 9 for a summary of both).

Science in Management of Protected Areas Association
Centre for Wildlife and Conservation Biology
Acadia University
Wolfville, Nova Scotia B0P 1X0
Canada
FAX: (902) 542-3466
Web site: http://www.sampaa.org
Contact: President

The Science in Management of Protected Areas Association is involved in improving approaches and scientific knowledge used to manage protected areas, biodiversity, and other related environmental qualities. The organization's conference proceedings are peer reviewed (meaning they are scholarly works that are checked and approved by other scientists) and can be ordered at the center's Web site. The 1995 conference proceedings dealt exclusively with marine protected areas and sustainable fisheries, but other editions are relevant as well, for they address concerns for protecting habitats and using ecosystem management processes such as integrated coastal management (see chapter 2).

U.S. Government Agencies

Coast Guard
2100 Second Street, S.W.
Washington, DC 20593
(202) 267-2229 (general information)
Contact: Commander

The U.S. Coast Guard is one of the five armed services, along with the navy, marines, army, and air force. Until November 2002, when the Coast Guard was brought into the Department of Homeland Security, it was part of the Department of Transportation. During war or at the president's discretion, the Coast Guard is under the direction of the secretary of the navy. The U.S. Coast Guard is charged with protecting the nation's coasts, inlets, ports, bays, and exclusive economic zones. Among the major duties of the Coast Guard are enforcing national laws in U.S. waters, aiding mariners in distress, providing national defense, and protecting marine natural resources by enforcing laws and treaties. The motto of the Coast Guard is *Semper Paratus,* or "always ready."

Environmental Protection Agency (USEPA)
Ariel Rios Building
1200 Pennsylvania Avenue, N.W.
Washington, DC 20460
(202) 260-2090
Web site: http://www.epa.gov/
Contact: Director

The Environmental Protection Agency (USEPA) is an agency of the U.S. federal government that regulates pollution and manages air and water standards. The agency was created by President Nixon as a way to reorganize the federal administration. The National Oceanic and Atmospheric Administration was created by President Nixon at the same time. The mission of the USEPA is to protect human health and "safeguard the natural environment." The USEPA divides the country into ten regions that are managed under the authority of federal legislation such as the Safe Drinking Water Act. Often, the USEPA will delegate regulatory authority to the states, providing guidelines for minimal acceptable limits of toxins and pollutants in the environment. In relation to the ocean, the USEPA provides oversight for all ocean dumping in U.S. waters through the Marine Protection, Research and Sanctuaries Act.

Fish and Wildlife Service
Main Interior
1849 C Street, N.W., Room 3251
Washington, DC 20240-0001
E-mail: http://contact@fws.gov
Web site: http://www.fws.gov

The U.S. Fish and Wildlife Service is a branch of the U.S. Department of the Interior. Its primary mission is to "conserve, protect and enhance fish, wildlife, and plants and their habitats for the continuing benefit of the American people." It is the only U.S. federal agency with such a mandate. As part of its organizational mission, the Fish and Wildlife Service is responsible for managing and protecting species on the Endangered Species List.

The agency is vital for U.S. ocean policy because included in its mandate is the conservation of marine wildlife and plants. One project it is involved in is the U.S. Coral Reef Initiative, which aims to protect U.S. coral reefs, such as those found in the Florida Keys. The agency is also involved in managing the Marine Mammal Protection Act of 1972, which regulated the taking of any marine mammal in U.S. water.

The agency has a history dating back to 1871, after Congress designated the U.S. Fish Commission to explore why U.S. fish stocks were decreasing. Also part of the agency's history is the Office of Economic Ornithology, which was within the Department of Agriculture at the time it was created in 1885. Later, this office was renamed the Bureau of Biological Survey, and its job was to survey food habits of birds. Ultimately, both of these offices were consolidated into the U.S. Fish and Wildlife

Service. One of the responsibilities the service inherited from the Bureau of Biological Survey was to survey the condition of the country's wildlife, which it does every five years.

National Oceanic and Atmospheric Administration (NOAA)
NOAA Central Library
SSMC#3, 2nd Floor
1315 East West Highway
Silver Spring, MD 20910
(301) 713-2600, ext. 124
Web site: http://www.noaa.gov/

The National Oceanic and Atmospheric Administration is an essential component of U.S. ocean management. The primary purpose of NOAA is to provide information and assessment of changes in oceanic and weather patterns, as well as living and nonliving ocean resources and environments. NOAA was created by President Nixon, along with the Environmental Protection Agency, to put the country's oceanic and atmospheric programs into a cohesive and unified administrative agency. Currently, one of the more important parts of NOAA is the National Marine Fishery Service (NMFS). This is the agency that implements the Magnuson-Stevens Fishery Conservation and Management Act and the Sustainable Fisheries Act, which divide the nation's fisheries into regions. The success or failure of these programs rests heavily on NOAA and the NMFS.

NOAA is a science-based agency whose history can be traced back to 1807 when President Thomas Jefferson charged the nation's first scientific agency, the newly created Coast and Geodetic Survey, to "survey the coast." This survey would continue to do coastal research until it was incorporated into NOAA in 1970 within the Department of Commerce. Other agencies to be incorporated into NOAA were the Bureau of Commercial Fisheries, the U.S. Weather Bureau, the Environmental Data Center, the National Satellite Center, and several research libraries.

NOAA also administers the National Marine Sanctuary Program. Created in 1972 within the Marine Protection, Research and Sanctuaries Act, this NOAA program administers U.S. marine protected areas much like the National Park Service manages parks and monuments. As of this writing, there are thirteen marine sanctuaries protecting some 18,000 square miles of marine habitat.

International Agencies

International agencies, also known as international governmental organizations, are usually formed/created a result of an international agreement. Each of the organizations listed in this section has an important role to play in governing and affecting ocean spaces. Since the World Ocean deeply affects and is affected by international politics, there are many relevant international governmental organizations; the list below is only a sample of the most important groups to ocean politics and policy.

Global Environmental Facility (GEF)
1818 H Street, N.W.
Washington, DC 20433
(202) 473-0508
FAX: (202) 522-3240 or (202) 522-3245
E-mail: http://secretariatofgef@worldbank.org
Web site: http://www.gefweb.org

The GEF is the world's largest environmental fund, and it is run out of the World Bank, which affects many ocean-related policies (see World Bank entry). Started in 1991 as an experiment, it was restructured after the Rio Conference on Environment and Development in 1992 as a permanent funding agency to reduce environmental degradation.

Intergovernmental Oceanographic Commission (IOC)
1, rue Miollis
75732 Paris Cedex 15
France
FAX: (33) 45-68-58-12
Web site: http://ioc.unesco.org/iocweb/

The IOC is a branch of the United Nations Educational, Scientific, and Cultural Organization (UNESCO), which was founded in 1960. As indicated on its Web site, this organization was founded on the belief that "the oceans, covering some seventy percent of the earth's surface, exert a profound influence on mankind and even on all forms of life on Earth. . . . In order to properly interpret the full value of the oceans to mankind, they must be studied from many points of view. While pioneering research and new ideas usually come from individuals and small groups, many aspects of oceanic investigations present far too formidable a task to be undertaken by any one nation or even a few nations."

The IOC is made up of 129 member states, 36 of which are on the Executive Council. The secretariat, as in many UN agencies, administers the program. The objectives of the organization are to promote scientific research, education, and leadership in understanding the environmental changes occurring in the ocean. Researchers can find information on harmful algae blooms, global climate change, and other important ocean problems on the group's Web site. Also available on the IOC Web site are lists of experts pertaining to specific problems. For harmful algae blooms, the agency provides a list of public health officials, scientists, physicians, and others who could potentially help deal with the associated risks of algae blooms. This is done to speed the access of information across borders, which is one of the organizational missions of the IOC.

The IOC is also a force in encouraging the implementation and understanding of integrated coastal management. It supported the publication of the primary reference in the field, *Integrated Coastal and Ocean Management, Concepts and Practices,* which was written by Biliana Cicin-Sain and Robert Knecht and published in 1998. It also continues to publish methodological guides for assessing coastal zone issues, as well as practical, step-by-step guides to using this management technique. On the IOC Web site, researchers can find connections to important international events that relate to regional planning and coastal management, as well as global events that pertain to these practices.

Intergovernmental Panel on Climate Change (IPCC)
c/o World Meteorological Organization
7bis Avenue de la Paix
C.P. 2300
CH-1211, Geneva 2, Switzerland
41 (22) 7308208 or 41 (22) 7308284
FAX: 41 (22) 7308025 or 41 (22) 7308013
E-mail: http://ipcc_sec@gateway.wmo.ch
Contact: IPCC secretariat

As a result of continued concern over global climate change, the World Meteorological Organization and the United Nations Environment Programme founded the Intergovernmental Panel on Climate Change (IPCC) in 1988. The IPCC is made up primarily of international scientists. The group's Web site says, "The role of the IPCC is to assess the scientific, technical and socio-economic information relevant for the understanding of the risk of human-induced climate change. It does not carry out research nor does it monitor climate related data or other relevant parameters. It bases its assessment mainly on peer reviewed and published scientific/technical literature." A great deal of evidence that the IPCC uses to demonstrate the phenomenon of climate change is derived from oceanic changes, such as the warming of ocean currents and sea-level rise.

Since global climate change has been a controversial issue and much of this controversy involves the quality of knowledge regarding influences on global warming, the IPCC has played a significant role in legitimizing the scientific evidence that supports the global-warming hypothesis. Within the organization, working groups meet to explore the scientific basis for climate change, the socioeconomic effects of this change, and possible ways to reduce elements that are forcing global climate change. The group meets once a year to adopt and confirm reports and plans, and it also publishes periodical assessments, such as *Climate Change 2001.*

International Center for Living Aquatic Resources (ICLARM). *See* **World Fish Center**

International Council for the Exploration of the Sea (ICES)
Palægade 2–4, DK-1261
Copenhagen, Denmark
45 (33) 15-2677
FAX: 45 (33) 93-4215
E-mail: http://ices.info@ices.dk
Contact: Secretariat

ICES is the oldest intergovernmental science organization in the world, started in 1902. It began as an informal science organization but now operates under a formal international treaty that was created in 1964. The organization now involves nineteen member states who have an interest in the North Atlantic, its primary area of interest. ICES operates a committee that advises on the management of fisheries and the marine environment, conducts international symposia, and holds many meetings about the North Atlantic each year as well as an annual science conference and meeting of the parties (member states).

ICES also has some of the largest marine databases in the world, including some fishery data that go back to 1900. Researchers can download some of these databases from the ICES Web site or request them from the secretariat. Other information available from the North Atlantic are data on water quality, information from the biological community, and a survey of trawler effects.

International Seabed Authority (ISA)
14-20 Port Royal Street
Kingston, Jamaica, West Indies
(876) 922-9105
FAX: (876) 922-0195
Web site: http://www.isa.org.jm/
Contact: Secretariat

The International Seabed Authority (ISA) is the agency responsible for managing deep-sea mining leases under the high seas. The ISA started to operate when the Law of the Sea went into force on November 16, 1994. The ISA collects lease fees from mining interests for the purpose of redistributing that income to economically disadvantaged countries. The ISA operates under the authority of two international agreements. The first is the Law of the Sea. The second is a side agreement specifically concerning deep-sea mining. Since major mineral leasing has yet to occur, the effect of the ISA has not been overwhelming to date.

Joint Group of Experts on the Scientific Aspects of Marine Environmental Protection (GESAMP)
International Maritime Organization
4 Albert Embankment
London SE1 7SR
United Kingdom
44 (0) 20-7587-3119
FAX: 44 (0) 20-7587-3210
E-mail: http://ksekimizu@imo.org
Web site: http://gesamp.imo.org/index.htm
Contact: Administrative secretary of GESAMP

GESAMP is a scientific body that was created in 1967 by several UN agencies, initially to advise them on marine pollution. Since 1992 and Agenda 21 (see chapters 2 and 9), the organization has focused directly on science affecting marine environmental protection in general, not just pollution. Reports can be obtained from GESAMP regarding protecting marine biodiversity, water quality, coastal ecosystems, general overviews of the state of the ocean, and other scientific but readable assessments. Among the agencies that GESAMP aids within the United Nations are the Food and Agricultural Organization (FAO), the Educational, Scientific, and Cultural Organization (UNESCO), the World Meteorological Organization (WMO), the World Health Organization (WHO), and the United Nations Environment Programme (UNEP).

Strategic Initiative for Ocean and Coastal Management (SIOCAM)
United Nations Development Programme
304 East 45th Street, FF-1086
New York, NY 10017
(212) 906-6690
Web site: http://www.sdnp.undp.org/siocam/

SIOCAM is run by the United Nations Development Programme (UNDP) as a way to train public officials in coastal management. Perhaps one of the more important projects SIOCAM has completed is their integrated convention management table, which is a tool for coastal managers to know about and attempt to comply with international environmental regimes, such as the Convention on Biological Diversity. The Web site version of this table provides a copy of the various conventions, their policy goals, and how to implement them. Such a contribution may sound simple, but the table is one of the first easily accessible documents that allows managers to connect the various international commitments to their own areas. Further, the compliance to international regimes has been a point of discussion since the beginning of regimes themselves, and most scholars agree that the "capacity," or ability, of a nation and its managers to interact and adopt treaty commitments is a major obstacle. SIOCAM and the UNDP both aim to improve the ability of countries (especially poor nations) to comply with international demands through cross-training and international exchanges of managers, the setting of practical guidelines for people on the ground, and exchanging information such as this convention table.

United Nations Division for Ocean Affairs and the Law of the Sea
Office of Legal Affairs, Room DC2-0450

United Nations
New York, NY 10017
(212) 963-3950
FAX: (212) 963-5847
E-mail: http://doalos@un.org
Web site: http://www.un.org/Depts/los/index.htm
Contact: Director

The primary mission of the Division for Ocean Affairs and the Law of the Sea is to provide information and advice to the secretary-general of the United Nations. The division operates within the United Nations Environment Programme (see entry). It is also the keeper of records regarding the Law of the Sea and consequently is where original sources for full-text versions of that law and its related agreements are available. Associated records that are available are the Agreement Relating to the Implementation of Part XI of the Convention (deep-seabed amendment), the Fishery Stock Agreement, and related judgments of the International Tribunal for the Law of the Sea. The division also maintains information on meetings of the parties, press releases, accession and ratification records, a list of experts, and a group of readily available arbitrators.

United Nations Environment Programme (UNEP)
P.O. Box 30552
Nairobi, Kenya
254-26-23-401
FAX: 254-62-36-92
E-mail: cpiinfo@unep.org
Web site: http://www.unep.org

UNEP, the primary environmental management agency of the United Nations, has several ocean projects and offices, one of which is the Division for Ocean Affairs and the Law of the Sea, which is detailed separately in the next entry. UNEP coordinates more than ocean policy areas; therefore, interested researchers may find UNEP a good starting place for investigating several global environmental problems, including forestry, urban environmental concerns, atmospheric problems, chemicals, land management, and energy policy.

UNEP, however, has particular importance for ocean governance and politics because it manages the Law of the Sea and the Regional Seas Programme, two of the more important instruments governing the oceans. The Regional Seas Programme provides a framework for managing regional oceanic problems, particularly pollution. Data on the regions and the member states can be obtained at the UNEP Web site. Another program that UNEP operates dealing with the ocean is the Global International Waters Assessment. The goal of this project is to assess the quality of and threats to international and transboundary waters, including marine, coastal, and freshwater areas as well as surface water and groundwaters. Included in the assessment's concerns are socioeconomic causes of water degradation in international areas; the implication of this work is that international relations regarding environmental changes and security can be proactively addressed in a cooperative way prior to a crisis. This project is also funded by the Global Environmental Facility (GEF) (see entry).

United Nations Food and Agricultural Organization (FAO)
Viale delle Terme di Caracalla, 00100
Rome, Italy
39 (06) 5705-1
FAX: 39 (06) 5705-3152
Telex: 625852/610181 FAO I/
Cable address: FOODAGRI ROME
E-mail: http://FAO-HQ@fao.org
Web site: http://www.fao.org

Founded in 1945, the FAO was charged with raising levels of worldwide nutrition (food security), standards of living, and agricultural productivity, as well as improving rural living conditions. As a part of its food security concerns, the FAO places a strong focus on fisheries, and it is the definitive source for global fisheries data, particularly in its annual "State of the World Fisheries and Aquaculture" report and the "One Fish" Internet portal (see chapter 9).

World Bank
1818 H Street, N.W.
Washington, DC 20433
(202) 473-1000
FAX: (202) 477-6391
E-mail: On the Web site
Web site: http://www.worldbank.org
Contact: President

The World Bank is part of the global financial regime set up in Bretton Woods, New Hampshire, in 1944. Its function is to make "development" loans, or loans that are intended to aid underdeveloped economies. The most important aspect of the World Bank in terms of the oceans is its support for the Global Environmental Facility (see entry); however, the World Bank is itself an actor apart from the GEF within ocean politics because it funds (often with some controversy) projects such as dams and oil development projects that directly affect environmental conditions of coastlines and other marine environs. In fact, as more people live near the world's coasts, more investments for developing these coastlines will be at issue. The World Bank is conscious of this tension and has experts that study the impacts of its investments on coastal areas, but controversy surrounding their loaning practices promises to be a part of ocean politics for a long time to come.

In addition to this influence, the World Bank is a good organization to be familiar with when doing international economic research. One of the organization's consistent publications is *World Development Indicators,* which is a statistical account of international and national economies. Thus, the World Bank is a relatively authoritative source of economic data that often frame the question, for better or worse, "What is a developing country?" This is a legitimate question for ocean scholars to consider, remembering that international ocean law was transformed as a result of politics between industrial and "developing" countries.

World Fish Center
Jalan Batu Maung, Batu Maung
11960 Bayan Lepas
Penang, Malaysia
P.O. Box 500, GPO 10670
Penang, Malaysia
(604) 626-1606
FAX: (604) 626-5530
Web site: http://www.worldfishcenter.org/

The World Fish Center—previously known as the International Center for Living Aquatic Resources (ICLARM), which was founded in 1977 in Hawaii—is a "food and environmental" research organization. According to the center's Web site, the organization's goals are to join forces "with farmers, scientists, and policy makers around the world to help the rural poor increase their income, preserve their environment, and improve their lives." The center supports conservation projects related to fishing, coral reef protection, and the use of living marine resources. It has outreach centers in Egypt, Malawi, the Philippines, Cameroon, the Caribbean, New Caledonia, the Solomon Islands, and Vietnam. Users can download the organization's quarterly publication, *Naga*, on the Web site as well as look at the latest scientific research that the center is conducting and publishing.

9

Selected Print and Nonprint Resources

Print Resources

Baretta-Bekker, Hanneke, Egbert Duursma, and Bouwe Kuipers, eds. 1998. *Encyclopedia of Marine Sciences.* 2nd ed. New York: Springer.

This book gives definitions to oceanographic terms and insight into the common language of marine scientists. Included in the book are major concepts, methods, and terminology of marine study. The work is meant to be used by students, teachers, and scientists from across multiple disciplines in order to reduce confusion in the multiple areas of marine inquiry. Entries range from biochemistry and biophysics to geology, biology, and general oceanography. There are many illustrations and explanations to make concepts clear to beginning students of ocean science.

Cable, James. 1994. *Gunboat Diplomacy 1919–1991.* 3rd ed. New York: St. Martin's Press.

James Cable's assessment and data on using naval force to manipulate foreign policy (as a tool *outside of war*) has been described as the standard in the field of ocean military security. This text offers definitions, principles, and precedents of gunboat diplomacy, as well as the historical, technological, political, and operational environments of naval force. However, one of the most valuable and notable sections in this book is the case-by-case accounting of seventy years of naval conflicts in the appendix, each event listed in chronological order. Each case is coded for the kind of force used, the conditions of the dispute, and, of course, the parties involved.

Gold, Edgar, ed. 1991. *Maritime Affairs: A World Handbook.* Essex, UK: Longman Current Affairs.

Although this book is becoming dated in some of its analysis (such as that on the Law of the Sea), it is still being used by ocean security analysts for its data on maritime conflicts. The text provides chapters on the physical setting of the World Ocean, the Law of the Sea, international maritime organizations and conventions, maritime transport and communications, living and nonliving resources, marine environmental protection, the coastal zone, and polar areas. However, the most valuable contribution that this text continues to make to this day is its documentation of strategic interests and dispute resolution for maritime conflicts.

Chapters that cover military strategy at sea and conflict resolution provide conceptual explanations on arms control, nuclear weapons, and other developments. Also, specific disputes are described, broken down by regions, such as the northwest Atlantic, the Arctic and North Pacific, Asian and Far Eastern waters, the Mediterranean, the Persian Gulf, and the Northern European seas. Each discussion of dispute contains an explanation and history, as well the final outcome if the dispute was settled by 1991. Finally, the text provides a set of rich appendixes, including a dictionary of Law of the Sea terms, a maritime reference bibliography, and a listing of maritime periodicals.

Hunter, David, James Salzman, and Durwood Zaelke, eds. 2002. *International Environmental Law and Policy.* 2nd ed. New York: Foundation Press.

The second edition of this reference/casebook is one of the principle texts for international environmental law students. The principles of treaty making and international environmental law are fully covered. There are vast sections on the air and atmosphere, freshwater resources, and oceans and seas.

The section on the oceans and seas provides in-depth information and discussion of the Law of the Sea and the Fishery Stock Agreement, and the full text for each is contained in the "Treaty Supplement," which comes with the reference. Other issues that are covered are hazardous waste and chemicals, wildlife and bio-diversity, international trade, and the protection of habitat and natural places.

The structure of the reference is in standard casebook form. Each topic has full-text portions of research articles by leading authors from a given area of expertise. Within these articles and the discussions that follow, the major operating concepts of the topic are fully explained through legal history and doctrine. The text is designed for advanced readers in international law, but researchers doing work in any of the topics mentioned here will find this reference helpful.

Mitchell, Ronald. 1994. *Intentional Oil Pollution at Sea: Environmental Policy and Treaty Compliance*. Cambridge, MA: MIT Press.

Winner of the Harold and Margaret Sprout Award from the International Studies Association (see chapter 8), Ronald Mitchell's book is an essential text for two topics: intentional oil pollution and environmental treaty compliance. Mitchell used the case of MARPOL (see chapter 2), the treaty that manages intentional oil pollution from ships, to evaluate what works and does not work for international environmental treaty compliance. He employed empirical evidence to create a useful and explanatory case study of the problem of intentional oil pollution and of noncompliance by nations who sign treaties. His key findings are that in order to ensure higher compliance with a treaty, the rules of that treaty must be easy to enforce. This book is part of a series published by Massachusetts Institute of Technology studying the problem of changing the behavior of nation-states.

Office of Sustainable Fisheries. 2001. *International Agreements Concerning Living Marine Resources of Interest to NOAA*. Silver Spring, MD: U.S. Department of Commerce.

This document explains a fairly comprehensive list of international agreements that pertain to U.S. marine interests. Fisheries receive particular attention. Although the work can be viewed as a reference for marine agreements, its most valuable contribution is its assessment of U.S. marine foreign policy, as described by the National Oceanic and Atmospheric Administration (NOAA). Also, a few bilateral agreements involving the United States are included; such material is typically left out of global treaty handbooks. This document can be ordered from NOAA, or it can be downloaded as a portable document at NOAA's Web site, http://www.nmfs.noaa. gov/2000int'lagrmts.PDF.

Sheppard, Charles. 2000. *Seas at the Millennium: An Environmental Evaluation.* New York: Pergamon Press.

This three-volume set is one of the most comprehensive environmental assessments of the World Ocean in print. *Seas at the Millennium* offers over two thousand clearly written pages of detailed descriptions and conditions of the numerous seas around the world, written by nearly three hundred authors. Contents of chapters include scientific data on regional and ecological problems, which researchers will undoubtedly find useful.

Each volume is dedicated to a theme. The first two volumes are divided into regional assessments, and the final volume covers global issues and processes of the world's oceans. The first regional volume is concerned with Europe, the Americas, and West Africa. Within this volume, complete analyses of most regional seas are available, including chapters on the Aegean, Baltic, Adriatic, Black, and North Seas. Many coastal nations within these regions have their own chapters, and some important bays, islands, and gulfs also receive individual attention.

The second volume consists of regional work involving "the Indian Ocean to the Pacific." Here, information is provided on the Red Sea, the Yellow Sea, the Cambodian Sea, and the Sea of Okhotsk. There are separate chapters for the Malacca Strait, the Gulf of Aden, the Gulf of Oman, and the northwest Arabian Sea, as well as numerous South Pacific island nations and African countries that have an eastern coast.

The final volume addresses categorical ocean environmental problems. Among the topics approached are the conditions of sea grasses, coral reefs, sea turtles, mangroves, climate change, cetaceans (whales, dolphins, and so on), fish and fisheries, and eutrophication. The volume also offers a few chapters on ocean politics, including the use of marine protected areas, future marine management, alternative energy from the ocean, global legal instruments of ocean management, coastal management, sustainability problems, and a final chapter on ecological economic functions and the social importance of the oceans by the well-known scholar Robert Costanza.

The primary usefulness of this reference work relates to the scope it provides. Researchers interested in a particular regional sea or coastal nation will likely find up-to-date baseline information that is difficult to find elsewhere.

Spalding, Mark D., Corinna Ravilious, and Edmund P. Green. 2001. *World Atlas of Coral Reefs*. Berkeley: University of California Press.

This publication provides one of the more up-to-date depictions of the status of global coral reefs. Data, such as the distribution of coral reefs, and other empirical observations are provided in maps and illustrations. The atlas is divided into several helpful sections, including one section that describes reefs in each area of the world. The role and importance, threats to, and processes of coral reefs also receive attention in this atlas, which is available in print as an oversize book, with portions found online at http://www.unep-wcmc.org/marine/coralatlas/contents.htm.

Stokke, Olav Schram, and Systein B. Thommessen, eds. 2002. *Yearbook of International Cooperation on Environment and Development 2002/2003*, Vol. 9. London: Earthscan.

Formerly the *Green Globe Yearbook,* this reference is compiled annually by the Fridtjof Nansen Institute (see chapter 8). It provides a systematic analysis and description of relevant environmental treaties and agreements and is available in some portion online at http://www.greenyearbook.org/index.htm.

The *Yearbook* offers a section on data and illustrations, international governmental organizations, international nongovernmental organizations, country profiles, and themes that are important in international environmental politics. The *Yearbook* is intended for a broad array of readers, from academics, journalists, and professionals to students. This publication is available in English and Chinese.

United Nations Environment Programme. 2000. *Global Environment Outlook 2000*. London: Earthscan Publishers.

Outlook 2000 provides a comprehensive review of environmental conditions all around the world, broken up into continents and areas of ecological concern. This text gives a state of the environment assessment for Africa, Asia and the Pacific, Europe and Central Asia, Latin America and the Caribbean, North America,

West Asia, and the polar regions. Each region contains a synthesis of numerous environmental factors, such as land and food, forests, biodiversity, freshwater, marine and coastal areas, atmosphere, and urban areas. The text also provides policy options for these areas as well as projections of problems for the future. Food security, water scarcity, and climate change are also given consideration in this reference.

United Nations Food and Agricultural Organization (FAO). 2001. *State of the World Fisheries and Aquaculture.* Rome: FAO.

Also known as the SOFIA report, this is the usual source cited for world fishery data. SOFIA is published every two years with the aim of providing policymakers and citizens with global, objective information on capture and aquaculture fisheries. The FAO breaks the report into global and national trends, singling out the highest-producing and highest-consuming nations, the distribution of fish uses, the size of the world fishing fleets, and the state of fishing equipment and its effects. Numerous graphs and tables clarify trends in fisheries, and the data is the most up-to-date that is available. The most recent three SOFIA reports are also available as a portable document at the FAO Web site, http://www.fao.org.

Van Dyke, Jon, Durwood Zaelke, and Grant Hewison, eds. 1993. *Freedom for the Seas in the 21st Century: Ocean Governance and Environmental Harmony.* Washington, DC: Island Press.

Although a relatively dated text, this book is still important for researchers investigating the Law of the Sea. The text was published one year before the law went into force, but the discussions that contributors offer on the subject of the treaty are relevant even today. Key experts on the treaty, including Elisabeth Mann Borgese and Arvid Pardoe (see chapter 5), address such issues as sustainability, the common heritage idea, common-pool resource management, and the ocean, and there is a good section on the Law of the Sea and its effects on ocean security.

Nonprint Resources

Databases and CD-ROMs

Databases contain bodies of literature and information that can be searched by using keywords. Many research databases require subscriptions. Often, libraries subscribe to several databases at a time in order to provide patrons with access to a given body of information. Online databases will frequently be offered as CD-ROMs, which may be more convenient for frequent users of specific data.

Aquatic Sciences and Fisheries Abstracts
http://www.fao.org/fi/asfa/asfa.asp

This large bibliographic database contains over 750,000 references centered on all types of aquatic sciences, including physical and social science findings through research papers and articles. The database is compiled in a cooperative effort by many organizations, among them the Food and Agricultural Organization, the Division for Ocean Affairs and the Law of the Sea, and the United Nations Environment Programme.

Database on the Introduction of Aquatic Species
http://www.fao.org/fi/statist/fisoft/dias/index.htm

This database permits searches for aquatic species that have been transplanted from one country to another. It is managed by the FAO (see chapter 8) and has a glossary of species introduction, as well as statistics on what or who "introduced" the species to the new area, the area of introduction, and the socioeconomic effects of this problem. There are also explanations as to the controversy of introduced aquatic species, the importance that this has to the industry of aquaculture, and the environmental consequences of this problem for biological diversity.

Environmental Knowledgebase Online
http://www.oxmill.com/ekol/

Environmental Knowledgebase Online contains over 600,000 citations relating to environmental issues. Within some citations are direct links to related materials that are helpful when doing topical research.

Environmental Treaties and Resource Indicators (ENTRI)
http://sedac.ciesin.org/entri/

ENTRI is an innovative database of tens of international environmental treaties, many of which are related to the ocean. The novelty of ENTRI is that it allows users to select several variables and correlate them to countries and treaties. Treaties can be arranged according to the states that are parties to those agreements and according to which agreements are relevant to a particular issue (for example, "fisheries"). This information can then be correlated with other variables, such as the value of the resource to each nation that is a party to a specific treaty. At a rudimentary level, users may see if a nation had little to lose by ignoring or approving a treaty and other important political questions. Users may also find the "remote sensing" images of some environmental issues of interest. Remote sensing is the compilation of maps and pictures that are made by "remote" means, such as aerial photography or satellite imagery. Among the data that are available on this site, users can view the creep of desertification (the phenomenon of increasing land area transforming into a desert climate) and the deforestation of the Bolivian and Pacific Northwest (U.S.) rain forests. Finally, another incredibly useful tool this database provides is a free text search of each treaty in its collection, which gives users the ability to perform a content analysis, or an accounting of any chosen word (such as *overfishing*) in any of these international documents.

ENTRI is provided by the Center for International Earth Science Information Network (CIESIN), which operates in coordination with several other agencies, including the National Aeronautics and Space Administration (NASA), the United Nations Environment Programme, the World Resources Institute, and the World Conservation Union (IUCN). The World Resources Institute provides the data for resources that are correlated to the treaty information on this site.

FishStat Plus
http://www.fao.org/fi/statist/fisoft/fishplus.asp

FishStat Plus is a program with data sets regarding numerous types of fish variables (for example, world fish catch). The UN FAO (see chapter 8) produces the data and the program, so the results and quality of this database are the most accurate available. FishStat Plus is specifically designed to run "time-series" data, or data that are recorded and mapped for trends over time (usually years). FishStat and the separate data sets can be either downloaded from the Web site or ordered as a CD-ROM.

Marine Environmental Education and Research, Inc.
http://www.meer.org/cdroms.htm

Marine Environmental Education and Research, Inc., offers CD-ROM titles on physical data on the seas and oceans, marine biology, wildlife conservation, and coral reef maps. These data can be acquired for free by eligible schools. They may also be accessed at the organization's Web site.

Pacific Institute Website
http://www.pacinst.org/nexus.html

This Web site, run by the Pacific Institute (which tracks the connections of environment and security), offers a bibliographic list of full text articles on environmental security. This list includes work by leading academics in the field, classic articles on the subject, discussions of controversies, and work by staff members at the Pacific Institute. Also on this Web site, users will find a directory of governmental, nongovernmental, and academic sites that relate to environmental security.

The Red List
http://www.redlist.org

The World Conservation Union (IUCN) (see chapter 8) maintains this list of the world's endangered species. It is considered among the most reliable sources of this information. The Red List provides data on many variables of endangered and threatened species, which can be sorted by country, by habitat, or by taxonomic group (phyla, species, and so on). Under the list, species trends (for example, whether a given species is declining, coming back, or staying the same) can be understood, as well as the general quality of the data that inform this assessment. Five important levels of endangerment are used on this list, including species that are considered extinct (no more individuals are believed to exist anywhere in the world), extinct in the wild (the species exists but only in captivity), critically endangered (the species are in danger of becoming extinct soon), endangered (the species face becoming critically endangered), vulnerable (the species face becoming endangered in the future), and low-vulnerability species (in less danger of becoming listed as vulnerable but are being monitored). The Red List is available on the organization's Web site or can be ordered on CD-ROM.

ReefBase
http://www.reefbase.org/

ReefBase is an online reef database run by the World Fish Center (see chapter 8). The purpose of this resource is to provide reef information to policymakers, researchers, and students. What sets ReefBase apart as an important resource is the fact that users can access the online GIS (global information system). With the online GIS, it is possible to create maps on demand by area, theme (for example, fish consumption of the area), mangrove area, coral disease, marine protected areas, and other interesting variables. ReefBase is a rich site with a great deal of depth; there is a lot to take from this resource, including detailed biodiversity reports by country or by region and policy recommendations that include data collection and protection of marine areas.

Sea Level Rise: History and Consequences (2001)

Accompanying the text of the same name written by Bruce Douglas, Michael Kearney, and Stephen Leatherman and published by Academic Press, this CD-ROM provides several layers of data on hundreds of sea levels. Between the book and CD-ROM data, a complete reference on the subject of rising tides is offered; data from this reference suggest there has been an overall global sea-level rise of 2 millimeters (or .078 inches) per year since the beginning of the twentieth century. Previous estimates were lower, but these data are the most up-to-date, since they account for "glacial isostatic adjustment" whereas other research has not. This glacial adjustment is the amount that some landmasses are "rebounding" from the effects of previous glacial weight. This phenomenon occurs because when glaciers were present in very large areas, they were so heavy that they pressed the ground down. When the last ice age ended, these large glaciers receded, and to this day, the land continues to regain its original height. This would have the effect of making sea-level rise look smaller because the land is rising also; taking this into account, scientists can get a more accurate understanding of the extent of sea-level rise.

A Sea of Troubles

http://gesamp.imo.org/no70/index.htm

A Sea of Troubles is a comprehensive report on the physical conditions of the World Ocean and includes several political components, including commerce and military issues, causes of problems, and suggestions and solutions to these problems. It is produced by the Joint Group of Experts for Marine Environmental Protection (see chapter 8). Areas that the report addresses are: marine water quality as affected by pollution, eutrophication, and altered sediment flows; life in the seas, including fisheries, biodiversity, coral, and alien species; and ocean- and atmosphere-related issues such as global warming, ultraviolet light, and nitrogen.

Seaweb

http://seaweb.org

Seaweb is a public education initiative aimed at ocean conservation. On this Web site, there are several resources that are helpful to researchers. One is a bibliography of ocean citations organized both by date and by topic, such as references for harmful algae blooms published in 1999, 2000, 2001, and so forth. Also, some full-text ocean-related "background" articles are provided. Finally, users may view the "Ocean Briefing Book" online. This resource offers a brief look at specific problems, synthesized into easily readable parts.

Unaami Data Collection

http://www.unaami.noaa.gov/

Unaami, the word of the Yup'ik people for "tomorrow," is a database resulting from the Study of Environmental Arctic Change, a project funded by the National Oceanic and Atmospheric Administration, the Polar Science Center, and the National Science Foundation. The project is an interdisciplinary effort to understand the interrelated changes that are occurring in the Arctic. The data sets (metadata) are available to researchers for further work, but the Web site can also help interested students and scholars analyze and sort some of the data on oceanographic changes, such as fisheries, marine mammals, sea ice, atmosphere, and other components. From this Web site, the Unaami database can correlate changes over a time series, some of which begins in the 1960s. Also, a bibliography of scholarly articles that have resulted from the database is available. Finally, researchers can create their own graphs using these data.

World Ocean Database
http://www.nodc.noaa.gov/OC5/WOD01/pr_wod01.html

This database contains geographically situated information about marine physical characteristics, such as depth, salinity, oxygen profiles, and plankton concentration. The World Ocean Database is provided by the Ocean Climate Laboratory through a CD-ROM, which can be accessed on the World Wide Web.

Computer Networks and Internet Resources

Agenda 21
http://www.un.org/esa/sustdev/agenda21text.htm

Users may view the entire text of Agenda 21, the document on sustainable development that was developed in 1992 at the Rio Conference on Environment and Development. Chapter 17 is a landmark document on "oceans and all kinds of seas," partially reproduced in chapter 7 of this book. Agenda 21 was ratified by over 100 nations and is one of the guiding agreements for global environmental affairs. The agreement is a benchmark for environmental goals but contains few guarantees of successful implementation.

Alaskan Oil Spill Site
http://www.oilspill.state.ak.us/

This Web site pertains to the *Exxon Valdez* oil spill of 1989 and is maintained by the *Exxon Valdez* Oil Spill Trustee Council, which was created as a watchdog group by Congress as a result of the spill. The purpose of this site is to provide a clearinghouse of information for students, teachers, and researchers interested in the spill and making sure that the disaster is kept in the forefront of the historical record as an example of mistakes made. Explanations of what happened during the spill, the ecological damage that resulted, and the current condition of the Alaskan coastline are all available at this official Web site.

The Environmental Sustainability Index
http://www.ciesin.columbia.edu/indicators/ESI/

The Environmental Sustainability Index is an innovative new tool to assess 140 nations' efforts at sustainable practices and development. The index is a project of the World Economic Forum, Columbia University, and Yale University. It operates by measuring twenty variables that have an environmental impact, from carbon emissions to subsidies of the fishing industry. The 2002 index finds that no country scores above average in all twenty variables, but the five highest-ranking countries were Finland, Norway, Sweden, Canada, and Switzerland. The five lowest-ranking countries in 2002 were Haiti, Iraq, North Korea, Kuwait, and the United Arab Emirates. This resource is remarkable because it is among the first efforts to quantify global environmental political dimensions, whereas most efforts to date have been case studies that cannot be generalized.

Fish Information and Services (FIS)
http://fis.com

FIS provides market-based information for the fishing industry. At this source, users will find price information (for example, on how much a tuna is worth today), national market information, fish news, and fishing technology information. Some aspects of this service are free, and some are available by paid membership. Fishing industry market information includes companies that deal in fish, fish-processing plants, aquaculture information, and important government agencies worldwide that relate to the fishing industry.

Harvard University Center for the Environment
http://environment.harvard.edu/guides/intenvpol/

Harvard's Web site allows users to conduct in-depth research into several international environmental areas. Many treaties are available on this site, and the information on each treaty provides a synopsis, the full text, and several sections of references for technical, economic, and scientific information relevant to the treaty. The site is meant to be a reference for those doing research at Harvard University's library, but it is open and available to any user.

Integrated Coastal Management Web Service
http://icm.noaa.gov

Funded in part by NOAA, the IOC, the World Bank, the United Nations Development Programme (UNDP), the National Ocean

Service, and the Center for the Study of Marine Policy at the University of Delaware (see chapter 8), this site is unique in that it provides practical lessons learned, case studies, national profiles, national ocean laws, and links to the most contemporary coastal management research. Researchers and practitioners of integrated coastal management can access suggestions for mitigating coral reef damage, developing and containing ecotourism, and reducing coastal hazards.

oneFish Internet Portal
http://www.onefish.org/index.html

Operated by the United Nations Food and Agricultural Organization (FAO) (see chapter 8), oneFish is designed to be a one-stop Web site for global fishery information. At oneFish, information is available on the global economy, ocean governance, professional organizations, conferences, and associations, as well as a great deal of other kinds of information.

The Pilot Analysis of Global Ecosystems
http://www.wri.org/wr2000/coast_page.html

The Pilot Analysis of Global Ecosystems (PAGE) is a project completed by the World Resources Institute. Authors Lauretta Burke, Yumiko Kura, Ken Kassem, Carmen Revenga, Mark Spalding, and Don McAllister have documented several global environmental changes that are occurring, and provide a section on coastal changes. Within the coastal issues, they examine coral reef threats, water quality problems, shoreline damage, losses in biodiversity, and food production. Though this resource is available in print, the online version has a phenomenal Power Point Internet presentation with maps that may be of use for classrooms with access to the Web.

Piracy Reporting Center
http://www.iccwbo.org/ccs/menu_imb_piracy.asp

The Piracy Reporting Center is operated by the International Maritime Bureau (IMB), which is a branch of the International Chamber of Commerce. The center is operated out of Kuala Lumpur, where it monitors and gathers information about piracy acts. The center provides a "weekly piracy report" where users may read about specific cases of piracy. This is the same information that is broadcast to ship captains so that they may be wary of activity in specific regions. As of this writing, the IMB is the primary source of piracy data.

Protected Area Database
http://www.unep-wcmc.org/protected_areas/data/nat2.htm

Operated by the United Nations Environment Programme with help from the World Conservation Union (see chapter 8), the Protected Areas Database is the most authoritative resource for getting lists of protected areas by country. Results of searches on this site can include in-depth information on the history of each protected area, as well as the political environment and policy directions of that country that affect the management of each protected area.

Reefs at Risk: A Map-based Indicator of Threats to the World's Coral Reefs
http://www.wri.org

One of the more comprehensive assessments of world coral reef areas, Reefs at Risk provides information on threats to reefs, projected assessments of reef survival, and clear explanations on the importance of reefs. Included are the first global maps of coral reef areas, coral reef threats such as bleaching and harmful fishing, and marine protected areas. Regional summaries, as well as in-depth consideration of twelve specific reef areas, are also provided. This work was published in 1998 and is available in portable document format at the Web site.

Threatened Animals of the World
http://www.wcmc.org.uk/data/database/rl_anml_combo.html

Threatened Animals of the World is a database operated by a branch of the United Nations Environment Programme (see chapter 8) that allows users to search for animals threatened with extinction. Searches can be organized at the phylum, class, order, family, genus, or species level, as well as through common names. There are also some illustrative tables on threatened species broken down by country and other factors.

Videotapes, DVDs, and Films

Blue Revolution Series
Type: VHS videocassette
Length: 16 30-minute parts

Date: 1990–2000
Cost: U.S.$2,145.95
Source: Films for the Humanities and Sciences
(800) 257-5726
P.O. Box 2053
Princeton, NJ 08543-2053
http//www.films.com

Blue Revolution is a comprehensive ocean series produced by Films for the Humanities. The series contains sixteen half-hour parts, which will be briefly described here. The series has won multiple awards, is endorsed by the National Education Association, and can be ordered through http://www.films.com/Films_ Home/Index.cfm?S=1.

In the Blood of Man: The Sea of Imagination explores historical relationships of Polynesian, Greek, Viking, Chinese, and Arab civilizations to the ocean through social values, commerce, warfare, and navigation.

Three films document global maritime commerce. *Worlds beyond the Sea* provides a history of European exploration and a technological advance that opened the way for global commerce. *Blue Highways: Trade Routes across the Seas* directs its focus at commerce also, with chapters on the Portuguese, Japanese, and Dutch merchant fleets. *The Container Revolution* explains how the container ship has revolutionized ocean commerce by making shipping more efficient.

Two films examine fishing. *The Last Hunters: The Cod Wars* looks at human exploitation and controversy over fishing. The film traces the history of overfishing from Grotius's mare liberum doctrine to the 1970s military disputes between Iceland and Great Britain, known as the cod wars (see chapter 3). *Farming the Sea* examines the issues of aquaculture.

With regard to the weather and climate, *The Return of the Child: The Effects of El Niño* explains and traces the history of El Niño, the weather pattern of a warmer Pacific Ocean around December-January that was first noted in 1982. The effects of El Niño, such as its connections to drought in Southeast Asia, dust storms in Australia, and pounding waves and rain on the Pacific Coast of the United States are also introduced. Also, *Mapping the Weather* provides basic information about the connections and workings of weather and climate, the complex chemical and physical interactions, and the effects that these connections have on human individuals and social structures.

Several parts of the series deal with international security and naval history. *Struggle for the Seas: The Development of Fighting Ships* portrays the first important naval battles, going back to 480 B.C. when Greek ships confronted Persian ships and to the sixteenth century when the British defeated the Spanish Armada in 1588. *The Modern Navy* tracks nineteenth-century ships to the present day, starting with the Battle of Trafalgar and ending with a profile and analysis of aircraft carriers.

Treasures of Neptune: Klondike on the Ocean Floor discusses the various opportunities and wealth that is found on the ocean floor, as well as the ecological effects of extracting these riches, which vary from pearls in oysters to oil.

Whose Sea Is This? asks questions about common-pool resources and specifically addresses the Law of the Sea and the barriers to countries to "do what must be done."

The Healing Sea: Life under Water poses the question, "If life started at sea, what secrets of contemporary life can we gather from it?" From this starting point, the issue of biodiversity is explored and put into an oceanic context. On a related topic, *The Frontier of Biomedicine* looks at the medical advances and research benefits that oceanic organisms have given human researchers and promise to give in the future.

The Ocean Planet: The Death of the Mississippi poses tough questions about the commitment of the United States to protect rivers, estuaries, and bayous from pollutants such as lead, mercury, and fertilizers that the Mississippi is now saddled with despite its designation as a "wild and scenic river." Also related to pollution issues, *The Ocean Sink* visits sites around the world to show the effects of wanton dumping, and it uses the Minimata disaster (see chapter 5) as a poignant example of human dependence on clean oceans.

Empty Oceans, Empty Nets (2002)
Type: DVD/VHS videocassette
Length: 60 minutes
Date: 2002
Cost: U.S.$24.98
Source: PBS Home Video
(877) PBS-SHOP
P.O. Box 751089
Charlotte, NC 28275
www.shop.pbs.org/

Empty Oceans, Empty Nets is a documentary that uses several case studies to evaluate the condition of marine fisheries. Director Steve Cowan and producer Barry Schienburg purposefully engage the political controversies of sustainable fishery management in this film and incorporate the points of view of a wide spectrum of stakeholders on fisheries, among them commercial fishers and distributors, marine biologists, and other experts who describe the health of various fisheries. The film looks at several fisheries around the world (including those of the Atlantic swordfish, Atlantic bluefin tuna, Atlantic cod, Alaskan halibut, and Pacific salmon) to examine different facets of fishery management. For example, the issue of marine protected areas is taken up as it relates to cod and the issue of aquaculture is taken up in relation to salmon. This film would make a valuable contribution to courses in politics, economics, sociology, and biology.

Horizon: Volcanoes of the Deep (1999)
Type: VHS videocassette
Length: 60 minutes
Date: 1999
Cost: Inquiries for educational copies may be made to the address given here, but the BBC typically does not sell tapes of this series to the public.
Source: Horizon
BBC White City
201 Wood Lane
London W12 7TS
horizon@bbc.co.uk

Horizon is an authoritative science program produced by the British Broadcasting Corporation (BBC). This episode is remarkable because it documents research done on the deep-ocean "black smokers," which harbor one of the most unique ecosystems in the world. Black smokers are deep ocean thermal vents that provide a home for organisms that do not use sunlight for energy; rather, these organisms use a unique chemical formulation that provides them their energy to live. Black smokers are also very powerful in the amount of heat they produce; in groups, they are said to provide the same amount of energy as the largest nuclear reactors. The program can be accessed on BBC broadcasts, but video copies are only sold for educational purposes, which are available at http://www.bbcworldwide.com/vet/.

Ocean Oasis (2000)
Source: Available only in commercial IMAX theater.

Ocean Oasis is a large-format film, made with IMAX cameras that allow it to be shown on a screen that is two stories high. This film explores the Sea of Cortez and the Baja California desert. The Sea of Cortez is extremely deep and brimming with life, and *Ocean Oasis* uses this area to demonstrate the flow of the food chain. Within the film, Mexican ecologists guide viewers through the stark, interconnected ecosystems, and with the support of the San Diego Natural History Museum, Conservation International, and other nongovernmental groups, the film makes a decided plea for conservation. Grade-school teachers wishing to use the film in class can find a teacher's guide at http://www.oceanoasis.org.

Ocean Wilds (2001)
Type: DVD/VHS videocassette
Length: 60-minute episodes
Date: 2001
Cost: U.S.$24.98 for DVD (2 episodes); U.S.$19.98 for each VHS
Source: PBS Home Video
(877) PBS-SHOP
P.O. Box 751089
Charlotte, NC 28275
www.shop.pbs.org/

This series of documentaries took nearly ten years to produce and was photographed by the marine veteran Feodor Pitcairn in high-definition television (HDTV), an advanced digital format. Each of the five films in the series blends Pitcairn's personal commentary, the product of over thirty years of ocean experience, with scientific information and observation. The first film in the series (the documentaries need not be viewed in order) is *The Realm of the Killer Whales,* which documents orca feeding on herring and salmon among human fishers. Unique in this film are the observations of familial behavior and playfulness that apparently were never seen before. The second film, *Sperm Whale Oasis,* is a remarkable piece in that Pitcairn was able to gain proximity to a group of sperm whales in the Mid-Atlantic. Sperm whales stay away from humans because they live at extraordinarily deep levels and because they have become wary of humans as a result of the whale hunting in the past. *Creatures of Coral* is the third film. Pitcairn films coral reefs in Australia and captures the amazing whale shark, the largest fish in the sea, and the giant manta ray.

Gathering of Giants is a documentary on whale behavior, including behavior around humans, and it features humpback and orca whales. The final film in the series, *Oases in the Seas*, looks at the Galapagos Archipelago, which is famous for its unique marine and island species, including the only penguin species that lives at an equatorial latitude.

Sea Power: A Global Journey (1993)
Type: VHS videocassette
Length: 55-minute episodes
Date: 1993
Source: Out of print but available at some libraries

This video series by Maryland Public Television explains the power of the oceans and seas to influence human society. Within the series, several topics of ocean politics are explored, including naval power and its role in exerting a nation's will from afar, commerce and the role of oceans in connecting and creating markets, and the oceans as a common-pool international resource. The work is based on the book of the same title by Luc Cuyvers. One of the main points conveyed throughout the series is the role oceans play in the rise and fall of nations and empires. A full range of ocean politics is investigated in this series.

Secrets of the Ocean Realm (1997)
Type: VHS videocassette
Length: 300 minutes on five tapes
Date: 1997
Cost: U.S.$99.98 for book and video; U.S.$69.98 for video only
Source: PBS Home Video
(877) PBS-SHOP
P.O. Box 751089
Charlotte, NC 28275
www.shop.pbs.org/

Public Broadcasting Service (PBS) produced this five-volume set of documentaries that cover many ocean issues and phenomena. *Secrets of the Ocean Realm* focuses on interesting and dramatic marine species, including whales, sharks, and venomous ocean creatures. There is also a companion book of the same title that goes with the series. This video can be purchased at http://www.pbs.org/oceanrealm/products/index.html.

The Shape of Life (2002)
Type: DVD
Length: 480 minutes on four disks/60-minute episodes
Date: 2002
Cost: U.S.$79.98
Source: PBS Home Video
(877) PBS-SHOP
P.O. Box 751089
Charlotte, NC 28275
www.shop.pbs.org/

This eight-part series looks at the diversity, beginnings, and evolution of life on the planet. The first half of the series is centered on ocean species and their transformation. Each episode has a featured set of organisms. The initial episode looks at the emergence of the first animal, sponges. Later episodes trace the evolution of animal movement, anatomical developments, and complexity, as well as the move of animals to land. The last episode attempts to put humans into biological context by drawing comparisons between chordate (skeletal) and nonchordate animals. This video would be most appropriate in biology classes, where the companion book could also be used.

Acronyms

CLC	International Convention on Civil Liability for Oil Pollution Damage
CZMA	Coastal Zone Management Act 1972 (U.S.)
EEZ	exclusive economic zone
FAO	United Nations Food and Agricultural Organization
FCCC	United Nations Framework Convention on Climate Change
FSA	Fishery Stock Agreement
GESAMP	Joint Group of Experts for Marine Environmental Protection
ICES	International Council for the Exploration of the Sea
ICJ	International Court of Justice
ICM	integrated coastal management
IFQ	individual fisher quota
IMB	International Maritime Bureau
IMO	International Maritime Organization
INGO	International Nongovernmental Organization
INSCEA	Incidents at Sea Treaty
ISA	International Seabed Authority
ITLS	International Tribunal of the Law of the Sea
IUCN	World Conservation Union
IWC	International Whaling Commission
LL/GDS	Landlocked/Geographically Disadvantaged States
MARPOL	973/1978 International Convention for the Prevention of Pollution from Ships
MPA	marine protected area
MSY	maximum sustainable yield

NAMMC	North Atlantic Marine Mammal Commission
NGO	nongovernmental organization
OILPOL	1954 International Convention for the Prevention of Pollution of the Sea by Oil
OSPAR	regime incorporating the Oslo Convention and the Paris Convention (the latter is also known as the Convention for the Prevention of Marine Pollution from Land-based Sources)
PIC	Pacific Island country
SFA	Sustainable Fishery Act 1996 (U.S.)
SOLAS	International Convention for the Safety of Life at Sea
TAC	total allowable catch
UN	United Nations
UNCLOS	United Nations Convention on the Law of the Sea
UNEP	United Nations Environment Programme
WWF	World Wide Fund for Nature

Index

About the Authors

Peter Jacques received a dual B.A. in philosophy and film from Montana State University and an M.P.A. from Northern Arizona University, where he is currently finishing his Ph.D. in political science, studying global environmental politics. He has published in several areas of domestic and international environmental politics and policy, environmental security, and political economy.

Zachary A. Smith received his B.A. from California State University, Fullerton, and his M.A. and Ph.D. from the University of California, Santa Barbara. He has taught at the Hilo branch of the University of Hawaii, Ohio University, and the University of California, Santa Barbara, and served as the Wayne Aspinall Visiting Professor of political science, public affairs, and history at Mesa State College. A consultant, both nationally and internationally, on environmental matters, he is the author or editor of nineteen books and many articles on environmental and policy topics. Currently, he is a Regents' Professor of Political Science and teaches environmental and natural resources policy and administration in the public policy doctoral program of the Political Science Department at Northern Arizona University in Flagstaff. He encourages students interested in pursuing graduate studies in environmental policy to contact him.